Poisonous Plants OF CANADA

Gerald A. Mulligan and Derek B. Munro
Biosystematics Research Centre
Research Branch
Agriculture Canada

Publication 1842/E
1990

Canadian Cataloguing in Publication Data

Mulligan, Gerald A., 1928-

  Poisonous plants of Canada

(Publication / Agriculture Canada ; 1842/E)
Issued also in French under title: Plantes toxiques
du Canada.
Includes bibliographical references.
Cat. No. A53-1842/1990E
ISBN 0-660-13467-5

1. Poisonous plants–Canada. I. Munro, Derek B.
II. Canada. Agriculture Canada. III. Title. IV. Series: Publication (Canada. Agriculture Canada). English ; 1842.

QK100.C3M8 1990   581.6'90971   C90-099103-8

Cette publication est disponible en français sous le titre
Plantes toxiques du Canada

Staff Editor: Jane T. Buckley

ACKNOWLEDGMENTS

We thank Eva Gavora and the other librarians for their patience and diligence in obtaining for us originals or copies of the many references on poisonous plants, the authors of these publications for providing most of the information here, Jacques Cayouette for his expertise in scientific French, and Jean Clost for her accurate and cooperative typing of the manuscript. We also want to express our appreciation for the contributions of our colleagues and the many people who generously gave us verbal or written information on plants poisonous to humans and animals. We hope that our fellow biologists forgive us for our convenient separation of humans from other animals.

CONTENTS

INTRODUCTION

This publication contains documented evidence on all the native, naturalized, and cultivated plants of Canada that are known to have poisoned humans (Appendix 1) or animals (Appendix 2), or both. It is based on two earlier publications entitled *Vascular plants poisonous to livestock in Canada 1. A preliminary inventory* (Mulligan and Munro 1983) and *Wild and cultivated plants poisonous to Humans in Canada: A preliminary inventory* (Mulligan and Munro 1984). Suggestions and corrections sent to us as the result of these publications and additional information subsequently gathered from the literature have been included.

Much confusion exists as to which plants can cause poisoning to humans and animals in Canada. Some general publications dealing with poisonous plants either perpetuate erroneous information, or do not cite source data, or do not differentiate between plants causing serious poisonings and those responsible for minor or dubious poisonings. The most comprehensive and accurate sources of information on plant poisoning are Muenscher (1951, 1975), Kingsbury (1964), Hardin and Arena (1974), Kinghorn (1977), Keeler et al. (1978), Frohne and Pfänder (1983), Keeler and Tu (1983), Cooper and Johnson (1984), Lampe and McCann (1985), and James et al. (1988). Additional information on poisonous plants in Canada is included in Fyles (1920), Thomson and Sifton (1922), Bruce (1927), Montgomery et al. (1955), Campbell et al. (1956), McLean and Nicholson (1958), Johnston et al. (1965), Lodge et al. (1968), Johnston et al. (1975), Lamoureux et al. (1975), Fleurbec (1978, 1981, 1983, 1987), McIntosh (1980), Agriculture Alberta (1983), Looman et al. (1983) and Frankton and Mulligan (1987). Many plants and plant products, when they are handled over a long time, cause dermatitis in a small percentage of people. Only the most important of these plant are mentioned here; a comprehensive account of them appears in *Botanical dermatology* (Mitchell and Rook 1979). We have also excluded, from this publication, plants that cause injuries because of barbs and spines, poisonous blue-green algae, and plant products or plants (such as sweetclovers, *Melilotus* spp.) that produce toxic substances because of the actions of microorganisms. Plants causing hay fever are listed in Bassett et al. (1978).

Plant-induced poisoning occurs when one or more chemicals present in a plant produce an undesirable physiological response in an individual. The occurrence of poisoning by a particular plant species often varies. Some species of plants are toxic only at certain stages of their life cycle, whereas others are most toxic during only one part of the growing season. In some cases the entire plant is toxic but in others only the leaves, seeds, or seedlings contain toxic ingredients. Some plants cause poisoning only when toxic elements, such as selenium, occur in the soil. Other plants may lose their toxins upon drying. Some toxins are so potent that a single mouthful of the plants can rapidly cause death. Other toxins are cumulative, the effects only becoming evident when the material is consumed over a long period. Many poisonous plants are distinctly unpalatable and are eaten by animals only in times of extreme drought or under other conditions when normal forages are scarce or absent. Severe poisonings of humans also occur under very unusual circumstances, when people eat, over an extended period, large quantities of normally nonpoisonous plants.

The metabolism of individuals and their ages also determine the degree of plant toxicity. Some humans and animals are highly allergic to a given plant whereas others are immune or only mildly susceptible. Children and young animals generally are poisoned by a smaller amount of toxic principle.

Several broad classes of chemicals are responsible for the toxic reactions caused by plants. Organic toxins include alkaloids, glucosides, oxalic acid, and resinoids. In addition, inorganic toxins such as molybdenum, nitrates, and selenium, taken up from the soil by some plants, can accumulate in plant tissue to toxic levels. Some plants contain substances that can cause photosensitization in humans and animals. Plant poisons can cause short-term illness, violent sickness, or death. Some plants are suspected of containing carcinogens.

Many poisonings of humans are caused by house plants, cultivated garden plants, and ornamentals. However, some are attributable to native or naturalized plants. Most poisonings of animals are caused by plants native or naturalized in Canada. The most commonly reported plant poisonings of humans result from curious children eating fruits and plant fragments.

A review of the available literature has shown that problems exist for doctors, nurses, and veterinarians who have to diagnose and treat cases of plant-induced poisoning in Canada. The initial problem is in determining whether the symptoms are indeed caused by plant toxins. The second is in acquiring a positive identification of the plant involved. In addition, well-documented literature is often not available on previous cases of poisoning and treatment. Regional poison-control centres across Canada are the best sources of information on plants poisonous to humans. Information on livestock poisoning can be obtained from federal and provincial agencies and from many universities and colleges.

When obtaining plant material for identification purposes, try to collect fresh leaves, branches, flowers, and fruits. Dry the plant material in a press or put the plants in newspaper and press under books or bricks in a warm dry place. Provide information on the habitat of the plants, the location and the date of the collection, symptoms of poisoning, and any other data that seem relevant. However, the urgency of the situation may require you to submit fragmentary material for identification. Plant identifications are available from federal and provincial agencies and from the biology departments of most universities and colleges.

Families, genera within each family, and species under each genus are listed alphabetically by botanical names. Common English and French names are taken, whenever possible, from *Common and botanical names of weeds in Canada/Noms populaires et scientifiques des plantes nuisibles du Canada* (Alex et al. 1980) and *Flore Laurentienne* (Marie-Victorin 1964). Additional French names of cultivated plants come from *Noms des maladies des plantes du Canada/Names of plant diseases in Canada* (Agriculture Quebec 1975) and from *A dictionary of plant names* (Van Wijk 1911). Local names of common plants may vary. The general distributions are according to Boivin (1966, 1967), except where more recent information was available. If a province or territory is identified in parentheses, the occurrence of the plant in that area has not been confirmed.

ALPHABETICAL LISTING BY BOTANICAL NAMES

ACERACEAE   maple family

Acer rubrum L.
red maple/érable rouge
Native and cultivated in Nfld., N.S., N.B., Que., and Ont.

Humans   No information on poisoning.

Animals   Signs of acute hemolytic anemia appeared in four adult horses 3 to 4 days after the ingestion of wilted leaves from cut trees (Divers et al. 1982).

AMARANTHACEAE   amaranth family

Amaranthus blitoides S. Wats. (= *A. graecizans* L.)
prostrate pigweed/amarante fausse-blite
Naturalized in southwestern Que., Ont., Man., Sask., Alta., and B.C.

Amaranthus hybridus L.
smooth pigweed/amarante hybride
Naturalized in southern Ont.

Amaranthus retroflexus L.
redroot pigweed/amarante à racine rouge
Naturalized in Mackenzie Dist., N.S., P.E.I., N.B., Que., Ont., Man., Sask., Alta., and B.C.

Humans   No information.

Animals   Poisoning and death of pigs and cattle have occurred after ingestion of these three species of *Amaranthus* (Gilbert et al. 1946, Whitehead and Moxon 1952, Buck et al. 1966, Osweiler et al. 1969, Duckworth 1975, Stuart et al. 1975, Hogg and Hibbs 1976, Weaver and McWilliams 1980).

AMARYLLIDACEAE   amaryllis family

Amaryllis belladonna L.
amaryllis
Ornamental, usually indoors in our climate.

Amaryllis vittata Ait.
amaryllis
Indoor ornamental.

Humans Recent evidence shows that rare poisonings are because of low concentrations of toxic alkaloids in the bulbs (Morton 1962, Lewis and Elvin-Lewis 1977, Frohne and Pfänder 1983, Lampe and McCann 1985).

Animals No information.

Clivia spp.
Kaffir lily/clivies
House plants.

Humans Poisonings are uncommon because of small concentrations of toxic alkaloids in the plants (Frohne and Pfänder 1983, Lampe and McCann 1985).

Animals No information.

Galanthus nivalis L.
snowdrop/perce-neige
Outdoor ornamental.

Humans Poisonings are rare because of small concentrations of toxic alkaloids in the plants (Lampe and McCann 1985).

Animals No information.

Narcissus poeticus L.
narcissus/narcisse
Indoor and outdoor ornamental.

Narcissus pseudonarcissus L.
daffodil/jonquille
Indoor and outdoor ornamental.

Humans Accidental ingestion of bulbs has produced several hours of severe discomfort. Handling large quantities of bulbs causes a dermatitis in some individuals (Wilson 1924, Muenscher 1951, Litovitz and Fahey 1982, Concalo et al. 1987).

Animals No information.

ANACARDIACEAE   cashew family

Rhus diversiloba Torr. & Gray
western poison-oak/sumac de l'Ouest
Native shrub in southwestern B.C.

Rhus radicans L. var. *negundo* (Greene) G.A. Mulligan
poison-ivy/herbe à la puce

Native shrub or climbing vine in southern Que. and southern Ont.

Rhus radicans L. var. *radicans*
eastern poison-ivy/herbe à la puce de l'Est
Native shrub or climbing vine in southern N.S., P.E.I., and southern N.B.

Rhus radicans L. var. *rydbergii* (Small ex Rydb.) Rehder
Rydberg's poison-ivy/herbe à la puce de Rydberg
Native shrub or vine in N.S., N.B., Que., Ont., Man., Sask., Alta., and B.C.

Rhus vernix L.
poison sumac/sumac à vernis
Small native tree in southern Que. and southern Ont.

Humans Sap from most plant parts produces an irritating dermatitis after an initial sensitization. In severe cases, death has occurred (McNair 1921, 1923, Krause and Weidman 1925, Shelmire 1941, Harlow 1946, Campagne 1949, Symes and Dawson 1954, Gaillard 1956, Loev and Dawson 1956, Epstein 1958, Kligman 1958, Klingman 1963, Mulligan and Junkins 1977, Guin 1980, Mulligan 1980a, Epstein and Byers 1981, Koch and Leon 1981, Polk 1981, Schwartz and Downham 1981.

Animals No information.

ANNONACEAE   custard-apple family

Asimina triloba (L.) Dunal
pawpaw/asiminier trilobé
Native tree in southwestern Ont.

Humans Contact dermatitis and severe gastrointestinal symptoms have occurred after the ingestion of fruits (Barber 1905).

Animals No information.

APOCYNACEAE   dogbane family

Allamanda cathartica L.
golden-trumpet/trompette dorée
Indoor ornamental climber.

Humans Weak evidence exists that the fruit is poisonous (Kingsbury 1964).

Animals   No information.

Apocynum androsaemifolium L.
spreading dogbane/apocyn à feuilles d'androsème
Native herb in Mackenzie Dist., Nfld., P.E.I., N.S., N.B., Que., Man., Sask., Alta., and B.C.

Humans   Sickness and death have resulted from its use for medicinal purposes (Fleurbec 1981).

Animals   Toxic to livestock when other forage is scarce (Muenscher 1975).

Apocynum cannabinum L.
hemp dogbane/apocyn chanvrin
Native herb in Mackenzie Dist., Nfld., N.S., N.B., Que., Ont., Man., Sask., Alta., and B.C.

Humans   Sickness and death have resulted from its use for medicinal purposes (Fleurbec 1981).

Animals   Toxic to all types of livestock, especially sheep, when normal forage is scarce (Muenscher 1975, Schuster and James 1988).

Nerium oleander L.
oleander/laurier rose
Ornamental shrub.

Humans   Poisoning and death have occurred. Cases of dermatitis have been reported (Halstead 1899, Kingsbury 1964, Der Marderosian et al. 1976, Lewis and Elvin-Lewis 1977, Shaw and Pearn 1979, Frohne and Pfänder 1983.

Animals   No information.

AQUIFOLIACEAE   holly family

Ilex opaca Ait.
American holly/houx d'Amérique
Ornamental under our conditions.

Humans   The only documented case of poisoning is a mild one that occurred after two young children ate "a handful" of berries (Rodrigues et al. 1984).

Animals   No information.

ARACEAE arum family

Anthurium spp.
anthurium

House plant in our area.

Humans Calcium oxalate raphides (needle-shaped crystals) in leaves and stems are injurious (Frohne and Pfänder 1983, Lampe and McCann 1985).

Animals No information.

Arisaema triphyllum (L.) Torr.
Jack-in-the-pulpit/petit-prêcheur

Native herb in N.S., P.E.I., N.B., Que., Ont., and southern Man.

Humans An intense burning sensation is produced in the throat and mouth if rhizome is eaten (Muenscher 1951, Kingsbury 1964, Lampe and McCann 1985).

Animals No information.

Caladium bicolor (Ait.) Vent.
caladium

House plant in our area.

Humans Calcium oxalate raphides in leaves and stems are injurious (Frohne and Pfänder 1983, Lampe and McCann 1985).

Animals No information.

Calla palustris L.
wild calla/calla des marais

Native herb in Mackenzie Dist., Nfld., N.S., N.B., Que., Ont., Man., Sask., Alta., and B.C.

Humans The whole plant, particularly the root, contains injurious calcium oxalate raphides (Frohne and Pfänder 1983, Lampe and McCann 1985).

Animals No information.

Dieffenbachia amoena Gentil
giant dumbcane/arum vénéneux

Indoor ornamental.

Dieffenbachia bausei Regel
dumbcane/dieffenbachia

Indoor ornamental.

14

Dieffenbachia picta Schott
spotted dumbcane/dieffenbachia tachetée

Indoor ornamental.

Humans Sickness and irritation of the mouth result from ingestion of leaves and stems. The name dumbcane refers to the temporary paralysis of throat muscles caused by calcium oxalate raphides (Barnes and Fox 1955, Pohl 1961, O'Leary and Hyattsville 1964, Walter and Khanna 1972, Der Marderosian et al. 1976, Lampe 1978, Arditti and Rodriguez 1982, Frohne and Pfänder 1983, Lampe and McCann 1985).

Animals No information.

Monstera deliciosa Liebm.
Swiss-cheese plant/philodendron monstéra

Indoor ornamental climber.

Humans Severe irritation and allergic reaction occur after ingestion of leaves and stems (Webb 1948, Der Marderosian et al. 1976, Lewis and Elvin-Lewis 1977).

Animals No information.

Philodendron spp.
philodendrons

Popular house plant.

Humans Raphides of calcium oxalate cause painful burning of lips, tongue, and throat. Because of the rapid onset of pain, plant material is rarely swallowed. Philodendrons also can cause a dermatitis on the skin of some individuals (Ayres and Ayres 1958, Dorsey 1958, Frohne and Pfänder 1983, Lampe and McCann 1985).

Animals No information.

Symplocarpus foetidus (L.) Nutt.
skunk cabbage/chou puant

Native herb in N.S., N.B., Que., and Ont.

Humans Raphides of calcium oxalate cause irritation of lips and oral cavity when leaves are chewed (Lampe and McCann 1985).

Animals No information.

ARALIACEAE   aralia family

Hedera helix L.
English ivy/lierre commun
Outdoor and indoor ornamental vine.

Humans   Poisoning after ingesting leaves and berries has been reported but none of the reports are recent. Some individuals develop a severe dermatitis after handling leaves (Muenscher 1951, Goldman et al. 1956, Kingsbury 1964, Forsyth 1968, Frohne and Pfänder 1983, Cooper and Johnson 1984, Boyle and Harman 1985, Hausen et al. 1987, Massmanian et al. 1988).

Animals   No information.

ARISTOLOCHIACEAE   birthwort family

Asarum canadense L.
wild ginger/asaret du Canada
Native herb in N.B., Que., Ont., and southern Man.

Humans   A few cases are documented of dermatitis after handling leaves (Muenscher 1951).

Animals   No information.

ASCLEPIADACEAE   milkweed family

Asclepias speciosa Torr.
showy milkweed/belle asclépiade
Native herb in southern Man., Sask., Alta., and B.C.

Asclepias syriaca L.
common milkweed/asclépiade de Syrie
Native herb in N.S., P.E.I., N.B., Que., Ont., and southern Man.

Asclepias verticillata L.
eastern whorled milkweed/asclépiade verticillée
Native herb in southwestern Ont., Man., and southeastern Sask.

Humans   No information.

Animals   Some poisonings and death of sheep and cattle are reported. However, livestock usually avoid eating milkweeds (Fleming et al. 1920a, Marsh and Clawson 1921, Reynard and Norton 1942, Clark 1979, Seiber et al. 1983).

BERBERIDACEAE   barberry family

Caulophyllum thalictroides (L.) Michaux
blue cohosh/graines à chapelet
Native herb in N.S., N.B., Que., Ont., and Man.

Humans   Berries and roots are cytotoxic (Lampe and McCann 1985).

Animals   No information.

Podophyllum peltatum L.
May-apple/podophylle pelté
Native herb in N.S., southwestern Que., and southern Ont.

Humans   One case is recorded of poisoning from young shoots; fruits can cause catharsis (Millspaugh 1887, Kaymakcalan 1964, Kingsbury 1964, Der Marderosian et al. 1976).

Animals   Poisoning and death of pigs and poisoning of cattle are reported (McIntosh 1928, Hansen 1930).

BORAGINACEAE   borage family

Amsinkia intermedia Fisch. & Mey. (= *A. menziesii* (Lem.) Nels. & Macbr.)
fiddleneck
Native herb in Y.T., Man., Sask., Alta., and B.C.

Humans   No information.

Animals   Poisoning and death of cattle, horses, and pigs are reported (Kalkus et al. 1925, McCulloch 1940, Woolsey et al. 1952, Kennedy 1957).

Cynoglossum officinale L.
hound's-tongue/cynoglosse officinale
Naturalized in N.S., N.B., Que., Ont., Man., Sask., Alta., and B.C.

Humans   No information.

Animals   Mention is made of the death of horses after feedings of grass hay containing hound's-tongue and of cattle poisoned by grazing hound's-tongue growing on waste land (Greatorex 1966, Knight et al. 1984).

Echium vulgare L.
blueweed/vipérine
Naturalized in Nfld., N.S., N.B., Que., Ont., Man., Sask., Alta., and B.C.

Humans Bristly hairs on leaves and stems can produce severe skin inflammation (Muenscher 1951, Lampe and McCann 1985).

Animals No information.

Heliotropium curassavicum L.
spatulate-leaved heliotrope/héliotrope obové de Curaçao
Native herb in southern Man., southern Sask., and southern Alta.

Humans Toxicity has occurred when used in herbal teas (Huxtable 1980).

Animals No information.

CAMPANULACEAE bellflower family

Lobelia cardinalis L.
cardinalflower/lobélie du cardinal
Native herb in N.B., Que., and Ont.

Lobelia inflata L.
Indian-tobacco/lobélie gonflée
Native herb in N.S., P.E.I., N.B., Que., Ont., and southern B.C.

Lobelia siphilitica L.
blue cardinalflower/cardinale bleue
Native herb in Ont.

Humans Sickness and death resulted when these plants were used for medicinal purposes in pioneer days (Millspaugh 1887).

Animals No information.

CAPRIFOLIACEAE honeysuckle family

Lonicera spp.
honeysuckles/chèvrefeuilles
Native, naturalized, and ornamental shrubs.

Humans Mild symptoms have been reported of feeling unwell and vomiting after ingestion (Frohne and Pfänder 1983).

Animals No information.

Sambucus spp.
elders/sureaux
Native, naturalized, and ornamental shrubs.

Humans Mild symptoms have been reported of feeling unwell and vomiting (Frohne and Pfänder 1983).

Animals No information.

Symphoricarpos albus (L.) Blake
thin-leaved snowberry/symphorine à grappes
Native shrub in Mackenzie Dist., N.S., (P.E.I.), N.B., Que., Ont., Man., Sask., Alta., and B.C.

Humans Berries are toxic if ingested in quantity. Mild symptoms are reported of feeling unwell and vomiting from other plant parts (Lewis 1979, Frohne and Pfänder 1983, Cooper and Johnson 1984, Lampe and McCann 1985).

Animals No information.

Viburnum opulus L.
Guelder-rose/obier
Outdoor ornamental shrub or small tree, sometimes naturalized.

Humans Mild symptoms are reported of feeling unwell and vomiting (Frohne and Pfänder 1983).

Animals No information.

CARYOPHYLLACEAE   pink family

Agrostemma githago L.
purple cockle/nielle
Naturalized in N.S., P.E.I., (N.B.), Que., Ont., Man., Sask., and B.C.

Humans No information.

Animals Seeds have caused poisoning and death of chickens (Quigley and Waite 1931, Heuser and Schumacher 1942).

CELASTRACEAE   stafftree family

Euonymus atropurpureus Jacq.
burningbush/fusain
Outdoor ornamental shrub.

Euonymus europaeus L.
European spindletree/fusain d'Europe
Outdoor ornamental shrub.

Humans Poisoning has been reported in Europe after eating berries; recent reports are of mild symptoms (Long 1917, Frohne and Pfänder 1983).

Animals No information.

CHENOPODIACEAE goosefoot family

Bassia hyssopifolia (Pall.) Ktze.
five-hooked bassia/bassia à feuilles d'hysope
Herb, naturalized in southwestern Sask., Alta., and B.C.

Humans No information.

Animals Poisoning and death of sheep are reported (James et al. 1976).

Chenopodium album L.
lamb's-quarters/chénopode blanc
Herb, naturalized in Mackenzie Dist., Y.T., Nfld., N.S., P.E.I., N.B., Que., Ont., Man., Sask., Alta., and B.C.

Humans Poisoning occurred in Europe when lamb's-quarters was eaten in large quantities because of a serious shortage of food during a period of war (Cooper and Johnson 1984).

Animals Poisoning and death of cattle, horses, and pigs are reported (Gilbert et al. 1946, Whitehead and Moxon 1952, Case 1957, Buck et al. 1966, Bassett and Crompton 1978).

Kochia scoparia (L.) Schrad.
kochia/kochia à balais
Herb, naturalized in N.S., southern Que., Man., Sask., Alta., and B.C.

Humans No information.

Animals Photosensitization of cattle results in poisoning and death (Galitzer and Oehme 1978, Dickie and Berryman 1979, Dickie and James 1983, James et al. 1988).

Sarcobatus vermiculatus (Hook.) Torr.
greasewood/sarcobatus vermiculé
Native shrub in southwestern Sask., southern Alta., and southeastern B.C.

Humans No information.

Animals Poisoning and death are reported in sheep (Chesnut and Wilcox 1901, Couch 1922, Fleming et al. 1928, Marsh 1929*a*, Wilson 1934, Sampson and Malmsten 1935, Hershey 1945).

Suckleya suckleyana (Torr.) Rydb.
poison suckleya/suckleya
Native herb in Sask. and southeastern Alta.

Humans No information.

Animals Poisoning and death of cattle are reported (Thorp et al. 1937, Thorp and Deem 1938, Hershey 1945, Berry and Gonzales 1986).

COMPOSITAE   composite family

Centaurea solstitialis L.
yellow star-thistle/centaurée du solstice
Naturalized herb in southern Ont., Man., and Sask.

Humans No information.

Animals Poisoning and death of horses are reported (Cordy 1954, Mettler and Stern 1963, Ivie and Witzel 1983).

Chrysanthemum spp.
chrysanthemums/chrysanthèmes
Indoor and outdoor ornamentals.

Humans An allergic dermatitis, affecting mainly the eye area, is an occupational hazard for those handling chrysanthemums over a long period. Similar allergic reactions develop after prolonged contact with some other Compositae. One of the authors (Mulligan) developed a sensitivity after working with *Achillea* species (yarrows) for several years. Sensitivity to one species of Compositae often results in sensitivity to other composites (Frohne and Pfänder 1983).

Animals No information.

Chrysothamnus nauseosus (Pall.) Britt.
stinking rabbitbush/bigelovie puante
Native shrub in Sask., Alta., and B.C.

Humans No information.

Animals Livestock poisoning has been reported in California (Sampson and Malmsten 1935).

Eupatorium rugosum Houtt.
white snakeroot/eupatoire rugueuse

Native herb in central N.S., N.B., Que., and Ont.

Humans Sickness and death have occurred after ingestion of milk from cows that have eaten white snakeroot. There are no recent reports of poisoning (Moseley 1906, Jordan and Harris 1909, Wolf et al. 1918, Couch 1927, Hansen 1928a, Couch 1933, Moseley 1941).

Animals Poisoning and death are reported in cattle, horses, sheep, and goats (Moseley 1906, Jordan and Harris 1909; Wolf et al. 1918; Hansen 1924a, 1925a; Graham and Boughton 1925; Couch 1926a, 1927; Hansen 1928b, 1928c; Marsh 1929b; Couch 1933; Moseley 1941; Doyle and Walkley 1949; Campagne 1956; Kaufmann 1982; Olson et al. 1984).

Gutierrezia sarothrae (Pursh) Britton & Rusby
broom snakeweed/gutierrezie faux-sarothra

Native perennial in Man., Sask., and Alta.

Humans No information.

Animals Cattle poisoning occurs during winter grazing when other vegetation is scarce (McDaniel and Loomis 1985, McDaniel and Sosebee 1988, Torell et al. 1988).

Helenium autumnale L.
sneezeweed/hélénie autumnale

Native herb in southern Mackenzie Dist., southwestern Que., Ont., Man., Sask., Alta., and B.C.

Helenium flexuosum Raf. (= *H. nudiflorum* Nutt.)
naked-flowered sneezeweed/hélénie nudiflore

Native herb in Que. and Ont.

Humans No information.

Animals Poisoning and death in cattle, horses, sheep, and mules are reported (Phares 1889, Pammel 1917a, Hansen 1924b, Ivie and Witzel 1983).

Hymenoxys richardsonii (Hook.) Cockerell
Colorado rubberweed/hyménoxys de Richardson

Native herb in southern Sask. and southern Alta.

Humans No information.

Animals Poisoning and death of sheep and to a lesser extent goats and cattle are reported (Marsh 1929a, Parker 1936, Aanes 1961, Ivie and Witzel 1983, Elissalde and Ivie 1987).

Iva xanthifolia Nutt.
false ragweed/fausse herbe à poux
Native herb in N.S., P.E.I., N.B., Que., Ont., Man., Sask., Alta., and B.C.

Humans Contact with leaves can cause dermatitis in some individuals (Muenscher 1951).

Animals No information.

Lactuca scariola L.
prickly lettuce/laitue scariole
Naturalized herb in N.S., P.E.I., N.B., Que., Ont., Man., Sask., Alta., and B.C.

Humans No information.

Animals Rare poisoning of cattle is reported (Beath et al. 1953).

Rudbeckia laciniata L.
cut-leaved coneflower/rudbeckie laciniée
Native, naturalized, and cultivated herb in N.S., P.E.I., N.B., Que., Ont., and southern Man.

Humans No information.

Animals Poisoning and death of pigs, sheep, and horses are reported (Anonymous 1874, Chesnut and Wilcox 1901, Pammel 1928, Skidmore and Peterson 1932).

Rudbeckia serotina Nutt.
black-eyed Susan/rudbeckie hérissée
Native herb, often weedy in artificial habitats in Nfld., P.E.I., N.S., N.B., Que., Ont., Man., Sask., Alta., and B.C.

Humans No information.

Animals Ingestion of large quantities can cause severe poisoning (Fleurbec 1983).

Senecio jacobaea L.
tansy ragwort/séneçon jacobée
Naturalized herb in Nfld., N.S., P.E.I., N.B., Que., Ont., and B.C.

Humans Toxicity has resulted from use in herbal teas (Lampe and McCann 1985).

Animals Poisoning and death of cattle, sheep, and horses are reported. Animals usually avoid grazing tansy ragwort (Pethick 1921, Clawson 1933a, Donald and Shanks 1956, Cooper and Johnson 1984,

Lampe and McCann 1985, Ralphs and Sharp 1988, Sharrow et al. 1988).

Senecio vulgaris L.
common groundsel/séneçon vulgaire
Naturalized herb in Mackenzie Dist., (Y.T.), Nfld., P.E.I., N.S., N.B., Que., Ont., Man., Sask., Alta., and B.C.

Humans No information.

Animals Sickness and death of horses fed hay contaminated with about 25 percent of common groundsel (Lessard et al. 1986).

Solidago mollis Bartl.
velvety goldenrod/verge d'or veloutée
Native herb in southern Man., Sask., and Alta.

Humans No information.

Animals Occasional death of livestock is reported (Beath et al. 1953).

Xanthium strumarium L.
cocklebur/lampourde glouteron
Naturalized herb in N.S., P.E.I., N.B., Que., Ont., Man., Sask., Alta., and B.C.

Humans No information.

Animals Poisoning of cattle, sheep, horses, and swine is reported. Other species of cocklebur are also poisonous (Marsh et al. 1923*b*, 1924, Hansen 1925*a*, 1928*d*, Forrest 1938, Reynard and Norton 1942, Löve and Dansereau 1959, Martin et al. 1986, Schuster and James 1988).

CRUCIFERAE mustard family

Barbarea vulgaris R. Br.
yellow rocket/barbarée vulgaire
Naturalized herb in Mackenzie Dist., Y.T., Nfld., N.S., P.E.I., N.B., Que., Ont., Man., Sask., Alta., and B.C.

Humans No information.

Animals One unusual case of poisoning of a horse is reported (Hansen 1930).

Descurainia pinnata (Walt.) Britt.
green tansy mustard/moutarde tanaisie verte

Native herb in Mackenzie Dist., Que., Ont., Man., Sask., Alta., and B.C.

Humans No information.

Animals Poisoning and death are reported of cattle foraging almost exclusively on green tansy mustard (Hershey 1945, Staley 1976).

Sinapis arvensis L. (= *Brassica kaber* (DC.) L.C. Wheeler var. *pinnatifida* (Stokes) L.C. Wheeler)
wild mustard/moutarde des champs

Naturalized herb in Mackenzie Dist., Y.T., Nfld., N.S., P.E.I., N.B., Que., Ont., Man., Sask., Alta., and B.C.

Humans No information.

Animals Occasional poisoning and death are reported of cattle, chickens, horses, and swine, mostly after eating large quantities of the plant or seed (Thomson and Sifton 1922, Gwatkin and Moynihan 1943, Mulligan and Bailey 1975, Cooper and Johnson 1984).

Thlaspi arvense L.
stinkweed/tabouret des champs

Naturalized herb in Mackenzie Dist., Nfld., P.E.I., N.S., N.B., Que., Ont., Man., Sask., Alta., and B.C.

Humans No information.

Animals Poisoning and death have occurred of cattle fed hay contaminated with 25 percent or more stinkweed. Photosensitization may also occur (Martin and Morgan 1987, Smith and Crowe 1987).

EQUISETACEAE horsetail family

Equisetum arvense L.
field horsetail/prêle des champs

Native herb in Keewatin and Mackenzie Dists., Y.T., Nfld., N.S., P.E.I., N.B., Que., Ont., Man., Sask., Alta., and B.C.

Equisetum palustre L.
marsh horsetail/prêle des marais

Native herb in Mackenzie Dist., Y.T., Nfld., N.B., Que., Ont., Man., Sask., Alta., and B.C.

Humans No information.

Animals Sickness and death in horses, sheep, and rarely cattle are reported (Rich and Jones 1902, Güssow 1912, Bruce 1927, Campagne 1956, McLean and Nicholson 1958, Cody and Wagner 1981, Cooper and Johnson 1984).

ERICACEAE   heath family

Kalmia angustifolia L.
sheep-laurel/kalmia à feuilles étroites
Native shrub in Nfld., N.S., P.E.I., N.B., Que., and Ont.

Kalmia polifolia Wang.
bog-laurel/kalmia à feuilles d'andromède
Native shrub in Keewatin and Mackenzie Dists., Y.T., Nfld., N.S.,
P.E.I., N.B., Que., Ont., Man., Sask., Alta., and B.C.

Humans   No information.

Animals   Poisoning and death of cattle, sheep, goats, and horses are reported (Marsh and Clawson 1930a, Clawson 1933b, Sampson and Malmsten 1935, Waud 1940, Pritchard 1956).

Menziesia ferruginea Sm.
western minniebush/menziézie ferrugineuse
Native shrub in Alta. and B.C.

Humans   No information.

Animals   Poisoning and death of sheep are reported (Marsh 1914, 1929a).

Rhododendron albiflorum Hook.
white rose-bay/azalée blanche
Native shrub in western Alta. and B.C.

Rhododendron macrophyllum D. Don ex G. Don
California rose-bay/rhododendron de Californie
Native shrub in southwestern B.C.

Rhododendron spp.
azaleas/rhododendrons
Native and ornamental shrubs.

Humans   Serious intoxications have occurred after children have eaten leaves or flowers (Leach 1966, 1967; McGee 1973; Hardin and Arena 1974; Cooper and Johnson 1984; Lampe and McCann 1985; Fleurbec 1987).

Animals   Losses of livestock after eating white rose-bay or California rose-bay are reported (Marsh 1929a, Gilfillan and Otsuki 1938, Knight 1987).

EUPHORBIACEAE   spurge family

Codiaeum variegatum (L.) Blume
croton/croton ou codier
Ornamental shrub or small tree.

Humans   Ingestion of bark and roots has caused irritation in the oral cavity, and contact with the latex has produced an eczema (Morton 1962, Frohne and Pfänder 1983).

Animals   No information.

Euphorbia cyparissias L.
cypress spurge/euphorbe cyprès
Naturalized herb, sometimes grown as an outdoor ornamental, in Nfld., P.E.I., N.S., N.B., Que., Ont., Man., Alta., and B.C.

Euphorbia esula L.
leafy spurge/euphorbe ésule
Naturalized herb in P.E.I., N.S., N.B., Que., Ont., Man., Sask., Alta., and B.C.

Euphorbia helioscopia L.
sun spurge/euphorbe réveille-matin
Naturalized herb in N.S., P.E.I., N.B., Que., Ont., Sask., Alta., and B.C.

Euphorbia lactea Haw.
candelabra-cactus/cactus candélabre
Ornamental shrub.

Euphorbia lathyris L.
caper spurge/cagarrino
Ornamental herb; naturalized in B.C.

Euphorbia milii Ch. des Moulins
crown-of-thorns/couronne d'épines
Indoor ornamental.

Euphorbia peplus L.
petty spurge/euphorbe des jardins
Naturalized herb in Nfld., N.S., P.E.I., N.B., Que., Ont., Man., Sask., and B.C.

Euphorbia tirucalli L.
penciltree/euphorbe effilée
Ornamental tree.

Humans The juice of any of these plants can cause a dermatitis on the skin or poisoning if ingested (Long 1917, Campbell et al. 1956, Kingsbury 1964, Worobec et al. 1981, Frohne and Pfänder 1983, Cooper and Johnson 1984, Frankton and Mulligan 1987, Stahevitch et al. 1988).

Animals Photosensitization from *E. cyparissias* and *E. esula* occurs in cattle, horses, and sheep, causing poisoning and death (Muenscher 1948; Case 1954, 1957; Johnston and Peake 1960; Johnston et al. 1965; Lorenz and Dewey 1988; Stahevitch et al. 1988).

Ricinus communis L.
castor bean/ricin

Ornamental tree.

Humans Chewing beans can cause poisoning and death (Malizia et al. 1977, McIntosh 1980, Frohne and Pfänder 1983, Cooper and Johnson 1984).

Animals No information.

FAGACEAE   beech family

Quercus rubra L.
red oak/chêne rouge

Native tree in N.S., P.E.I., N.B., Que., and Ont.

Quercus velutina Lam.
black oak/chêne noir

Native tree in southern Ont.

Humans No information.

Animals Poisoning and death of cattle, sheep, and horses occurs particularly when trees fall into pastures or in years when the crop of acorns is very large (Pammel 1917*b*, Duncan 1961, Sandusky et al. 1977, Cooper and Johnson 1984).

FUMARIACEAE   fumitory family

Dicentra canadensis (Goldie) Walp.
squirrel-corn/dicentre du Canada

Native herb in southwestern Que. and southern Ont.

Dicentra cucullaria (L.) Bernh.
Dutchman's-breeches/dicentre à capuchon

Native herb in N.S., N.B., Que., and Ont.

Dicentra formosa (Andr.) Walp.
western bleedingheart/dielytra à belles fleurs
Native herb in southwestern B.C.

Humans No information.

Animals Poisoning and death of cattle are reported (Black et al. 1923, 1930; Hansen 1930).

GINKGOACEAE ginkgo family

Ginkgo biloba L.
maidenhair tree/ginkgo
Ornamental tree.

Humans Severe dermatitis can result from handling broken or crushed fruits (Muenscher 1951, Baer 1983, Nakamura 1985).

Animals No information.

GRAMINEAE grass family

Glyceria grandis S. Wats.
tall manna grass/glycérie géante
Native and naturalized herb in (Y.T.), (Nfld.), (N.S.), P.E.I., N.B., Que., Ont., Man., Sask., Alta., and B.C.

Humans No information.

Animals Cyanotoxicosis and death in cattle are reported (Puls et al. 1978).

GUTTIFERAE St. John's-wort family

Hypericum perforatum L.
St. John's-wort/millepertuis perforé
Naturalized herb in Nfld., N.S., P.E.I., N.B., Que., Ont., and B.C.

Humans No information.

Animals Photosensitization in cattle, sheep, horses, and rabbits causes poisoning and death (Hansen 1928e, Marsh and Clawson 1930b, Sampson and Parker 1930, Gillett and Robson 1981, Crompton et al. 1988).

HIPPOCASTANACEAE   horse-chestnut family

Aesculus hippocastanum L.
horse-chestnut/marronnier

Outdoor ornamental tree.

Humans   Children have been poisoned in Europe after ingesting large quantities of nuts (Muenscher 1951, Frohne and Pfänder 1983, Lampe and McCann 1985).

Animals   Leaves and fruits have caused illness in cattle, horses, and pigs (Muenscher 1951).

HYDROPHYLLACEAE   waterleaf family

Phacelia campanularia Gray
California bluebell/phacélie de Californie

Herb, near Fort Saskatchewan, Alta., probably introduced from the United States.

Humans   Species with stiff glandular hairs produce a severe dermatitis in some people (Muenscher 1951, Munz 1965).

Animals   No information.

IRIDACEAE   iris family

Iris versicolor L.
blue flag/clajeux

Native herb in Keewatin Dist., Nfld., N.S., P.E.I., N.B., Que., Ont., and Man.

Humans   No information.

Animals   Poisoning and death of calves are reported (Bruce 1927).

JUNCAGINACEAE   arrow-grass family

Triglochin maritima L.
seaside arrow-grass/troscart maritime

Native herb in Keewatin and Mackenzie Dists., Y.T., Nfld., N.S., P.E.I., N.B., Que., Ont., Man., Sask., Alta., and B.C.

Humans   No information.

Animals   Sickness and death in cattle and sheep are reported (Fleming 1920, Fleming et al. 1920b, Marsh et al. 1929, Beath et al. 1933, Clawson and Moran 1937, Campagne 1956, Muenscher 1975).

LABIATAE mint family

Glechoma hederacea L.
ground-ivy/lierre terrestre
Naturalized herb in Nfld., N.S., P.E.I., N.B., Que., Ont., Man., Sask., Alta., and B.C.

Humans No information.

Animals One report mentions two horses being poisoned (Fyles 1920).

Leonurus cardiaca L.
motherwort/agripaume cardiaque
Naturalized herb in N.S., P.E.I., N.B., Que., Ont., Man., Sask., and B.C.

Humans Some individuals develop a dermatitis after contact with leaves (Muenscher 1951).

Animals No information.

LEGUMINOSAE pea family

Abrus precatorius L.
precatory-pea/abrus à chapelet
Seeds imported in necklaces and bracelets.

Humans Very poisonous; one ingested seed is fatal to an adult (Taylor 1962, Gunn 1969, Niyogi 1970, Davis 1978, McIntosh 1980, Hoy and Catling 1981, Frohne and Pfänder 1983).

Animals No information.

Astragalus bisulcatus (Hook.) A. Gray
two-grooved milk-vetch/astragale fondu
Native herb in Man., Sask., and Alta.

Astragalus lentiginosus Dougl.
Native herb in southcentral B.C.

Astragalus miser Dougl. ex Hook.
timber milk-vetch/astragale prostré
Native herb in southwestern Alta., and southeastern B.C.

Humans No information.

Animals Poisoning and death in chickens, horses, cattle, and sheep are reported. Teratogenic deformities in calves are caused by *A. lentiginosus*. (Beath and Lehnert 1917, Bruce 1927, Beath et al. 1932,

Trelease and Martin 1936, MacDonald 1952*a*, McLean and Nicholson 1958, James et al. 1968, Van Kampen and James 1969, Williams et al. 1975, Williams and James 1978, James et al. 1981, Ellis et al. 1985, Keeler 1988, Ogden et al. 1988).

Baptisia tinctoria (L.) Br.
wild indigo/indigo sauvage
Native perennial herb in southern Ont.

Baptisia leucantha T. & G.
wild false indigo/baptisie leucanthe
Native perennial herb in southern Ont.

Humans   The entire plant is toxic (Lampe and McCann 1985).

Animals   No information.

Gymnocladus dioicus (L.) K. Koch
Kentucky coffeetree/chicot du Canada
Ornamental tree.

Humans   One early report mentions a woman poisoned after ingesting the fruit pulp (Chesnut 1898).

Animals   No information.

Laburnum anagyroides Medic.
golden-chain/cytise
Ornamental shrub or small tree.

Humans   Although it is considered the second most poisonous tree in Britain, no cases of severe poisonings are documented (Long 1917, Forsyth 1968, Frohne and Pfänder 1983, Cooper and Johnson 1984).

Animals   No information.

Lathyrus sativus L.
grass pea/lentille d'Espagne
Food and forage herb.

Lathyrus odoratus L.
sweet pea/pois de senteur
Ornamental climber.

Humans   Both species can cause serious poisoning if used habitually as a food source (Stockman 1929, Selye 1957, Cooper and Johnson 1984).

Animals Both species can poison animals if fed over a long period (Stockman 1929, Selye 1957, Cooper and Johnson 1984).

Lupinus argenteus Pursh
silvery lupine/lupin argenté
Native herb in Man., Sask., Alta., and B.C.

Lupinus burkei S. Wats
Burke's lupine
Native herb in southern B.C.

Lupinus polyphyllus Lindl.
large-leaved lupine/lupin polyphylle
Native and naturalized herb in Nfld., N.S., P.E.I., N.B., Que., Ont., and B.C.

Lupinus pusillus Pursh
small lupine
Native herb in southwestern Sask. and southern Alta.

Lupinus sericeus Pursh
silky lupine/lupin soyeux
Native herb in Y.T., Alta., and B.C.

Humans Mild lupine poisoning occurred in Alberta when cooking instructions for purchased "edible lupine seeds" were not followed (Smith 1987).

Animals Poisoning and death of cattle, sheep, horses, and pigs are recorded. Although lupines are usually considered a valuable source of range forage, toxicity is unpredictable. Most of these lupines contain sufficient quantities of the teratogenic alkaloid anagyrine to cause crooked calf disease under some conditions (Marsh et al. 1916; Beath 1920, 1925; Couch 1926b; Beath et al. 1953; McLean and Nicholson 1958; Shupe et al. 1967; Keeler 1973, Keeler et al. 1977; Williams 1983; Davis and Stout 1986).

Oxytropis lambertii Pursh
purple locoweed/oxytrope de Lambert
Native herb in southern Man. and southeastern Sask.

Oxytropis sericea Nutt.
locoweed/oxytrope
Native herb in Y.T., (Man.), Sask., Alta., and B.C.

Humans No information.

Animals Poisoning and death of cattle from these locoweeds are reported (Marsh 1909, 1919; James et al. 1968; Van Kampen and James 1969; James et al. 1986; James and Nielsen 1988; Ogden et al. 1988; Ralphs and Sharp 1988).

Robinia pseudoacacia L.
black locust/robinier faux-acacia

Naturalized shrub or tree, sometimes grown as an ornamental in N.S., (P.E.I.), Que., Ont., and B.C.

Humans Sickness after the ingestion of seeds and inner bark has been reported, but there are no recent reports of poisonings (Emery 1887, Millspaugh 1887).

Animals Poisoning of horses, cattle, and chickens is reported (Gardiner 1903; Waldron 1908; Barnes 1921; Hansen 1924b, 1924c; Bruce 1927; Hansen 1930).

Thermopsis rhombifolia (Nutt.) Richards.
golden-bean

Native herb in Man., Sask., and B.C.

Humans Seeds suspected of poisoning children (Kingsbury 1964).

Animals Considered toxic to cattle and may cause teratogenic deformities in calves (Keeler 1983, Keeler et al. 1986).

Vicia villosa Roth
hairy vetch/vesce velue

Forage crop and naturalized in N.S., Que., Ont., Man., and B.C.

Humans No information.

Animals Poisoning and death in cattle are reported (Claughton and Claughton 1954, Panciera 1978, Kerr and Edwards 1982).

Wisteria species
wisterias/glycines

Woody ornamental twiners.

Humans Poisoning is reported in children after the ingestion of seeds or pods (Anonymous 1961, Jacobziner and Raybin 1961a, Kingsbury 1964, Frohne and Pfänder 1983, Lampe and McCann 1985).

Animals No information.

LILIACEAE   lily family

Allium canadense L.
wild onion/ail du Canada

Native to N.B., Que., and Ont.

Humans   Children who ingested part of plant suffered gastroenteritis (Lampe and McCann 1985).

Animals   No information.

Allium cepa L.
onion/oignon
Food plant.

Humans   A child, after ingesting nine stalks of onion, experienced a severe rash on face and body (Lampe and McCann 1985).

Animals   Poisoning and death are reported of cattle and horses after eating large quantities of onions (Goldsmith 1909, Thorp and Harsfield 1938, Hutchison 1977, Cooper and Johnson 1984).

Aloe spp.
aloe/aloès
Perennial house plant.

Humans   The latex is poisonous if ingested (Lampe and McCann 1985).

Animals   No information.

Colchicum autumnale L.
autumn crocus/colchique d'automne
Indoor and outdoor ornamental.

Humans   Burning sensation in mouth and throat is reported (Cooper and Johnson 1984, Lampe and McCann 1985).

Animals   No information.

Convallaria majalis L.
lily-of-the-valley/muguet
Outdoor ornamental.

Humans   All plant parts can cause sickness; however, the report of a child having died after drinking water in which lily-of-the-valley had been standing is unconvincing (Kingsbury 1964, O'Leary and Hyattsville 1964, Frohne and Pfänder 1983, Lampe and McCann 1985).

Animals   No information.

Gloriosa superba L.
glory lily/glorieuse du Malabar

Ornamental climber.

Humans Reports mention sickness and death after ingestion of tubers (Steyn 1934, Gooneratne 1966, Angunawela and Fernando 1971, Frohne and Pfänder 1983).

Animals No information.

Ornithogalum umbellatum L.
star-of-Bethlehem/dame d'onze heures
Outdoor ornamental.

Humans Nausea and intestinal disorders are reported in children after eating flowers (Cooper and Johnson 1984).

Animals No information.

Tulipa spp.
tulips/tulipes
Indoor and outdoor ornamentals.

Humans People can develop a severe dermatitis, called tulip finger, after constantly handling large quantities of bulbs (Frohne and Pfänder 1983).

Animals No information.

Veratrum viride Ait.
false hellebore/varaire vert
Native herb in Y.T., Nfld., N.B., Que., Alta., and B.C.

Humans Sickness and death are reported after the ingestion of plant parts (Boivin 1948, Underhill 1959, Anonymous 1972, Turner 1978, Boudreault 1979, Mulligan and Munro 1987).

Animals Sickness and death of sheep, cattle, and chickens are reported (Chesnut 1898, Chesnut and Wilcox 1901, Fleming and Schappelle 1918, Bruce 1927, Reynard and Norton 1942, Campagne 1956, Kingsbury 1964, Mulligan and Munro 1987).

Zigadenus elegans Pursh
white camas/zigadène élégant
Native herb in Mackenzie Dist., Y.T., N.B., Que., Ont., Man., Sask., Alta., and B.C.

Zigadenus gramineus Rydb.
death camas/zigadène vénéneux
Native herb in southern Sask., southern Alta., and southern B.C.

Humans Sickness and death are reported after ingestion of bulbs (Marsh et al. 1915, Cameron 1952, Spoerke and Spoerke 1979).

Animals Sickness and death in sheep, cattle, and horses are reported (Chesnut and Wilcox 1901; Heyl et al. 1912; Marsh et al. 1915; Fleming 1920; Fleming et al. 1921; Marsh and Clawson 1922, 1924; McLean and Nicholson 1958; Shaw and Williams 1986; Panter and Ralphs 1987).

LORANTHACEAE   mistletoe family

Phoradendron flavescens (Pursh) Nutt.
American mistletoe/gui de chêne
Sold around Christmas time. Native south of our range.

Humans Poisoning after the ingestion of berries has been reported but no serious poisonings are documented (Hymans 1898, Cann and Verhulst 1959).

Animals No information.

MENISPERMACEAE   moonseed family

Menispermum canadense L.
moonseed/ménisperme du Canada
Native herb in southwestern Que., Ont., and southern Man.

Humans Poisoning and death are reported after ingestion of grapelike fruits (Schaffner 1903, Gress 1935).

Animals No information.

MORACEAE   mulberry family

Maclura pomifera (Raf.) C.K. Schneid.
osage-orange/bois d'arc
Small ornamental tree.

Humans Some people have developed a dermatitis from contact with the milky sap (Muenscher 1951).

Animals No information.

OLEACEAE   olive family

Ligustrum vulgare L.
common privet/troène commun
Ornamental shrub.

Humans Children have been poisoned after ingestion of berries, but reports of death are undocumented (Long 1934, Kozlov and Gulyaeva 1983, Frohne and Pfänder 1983, Cooper and Johnson 1984).

Animals No information.

ORCHIDACEAE   orchid family

Cypripedium acaule Ait.
pink lady's-slipper/cypripède acaule
Native herb in (Mackenzie Dist.), Nfld., N.S., N.B., Que., Ont., Man., Sask., and Alta.

Cypripedium calceolus L.
yellow lady's-slipper/cypripède soulier
Native herb in Mackenzie Dist., (Y.T.), Nfld., N.S., N.B., Que., Ont., Man., Sask., Alta., and B.C.

Cypripedium reginae Walt.
showy lady's-slipper/cypripède royal
Native herb in Nfld., P.E.I., N.B., Que., Ont., and Man.

Humans Dermatitis can develop after touching the glandular hairs (Halstead 1899, Muenscher 1951, Reddock and Reddock 1984, Macaulay 1987).

Animals No information.

PAPAVERACEAE   poppy family

Chelidonium majus L.
greater celandine/grande chélidoine
Naturalized herb in (Nfld.), (N.S.), P.E.I., N.B., Que., and Ont.

Humans Severe irritation and gastrointestinal problems are reported, but the report of a death is unsubstantiated (Koopman 1937, Bandeline and Malesh 1956, Frohne and Pfänder 1983, Cooper and Johnson 1984).

Animals No information.

Papaver nudicaule L.
Iceland poppy/pavot d'Islande
Ornamental herb, occasionally escapes from cultivation and doubtfully naturalized.

Papaver orientale L.
Oriental poppy/pavot d'Orient

Ornamental herb.

Papaver rhoeas L.
corn poppy/pavot coquelicot
Ornamental herb, naturalized in N.S., (N.B.), Que., Ont., Man., Sask., and (B.C.).

Papaver somniferum L.
opium poppy/pavot somnifère
Ornamental herb.

Humans Toxic substances are present in foliage and pods (Kingsbury 1964, Frohne and Pfänder 1983, Cooper and Johnson 1984)

Animals No information.

PHYTOLACCACEAE pokeweed family

Phytolacca americana L.
pokeweed/phytolaque d'Amérique
Native herb in southwestern Que. and southwestern Ont.

Humans This plant has caused severe poisoning when used as folk medicine (French 1900, Sauer 1950, Lewis and Smith 1979, Jaeckle and Freemon 1981).

Animals Poisoning of pigs and turkeys is reported (Patterson 1929, Hansen 1930, Barnett 1975).

PINACEAE pine family

Pinus ponderosa Dougl.
ponderosa pine/pin ponderosa
Native tree in B.C.

Humans No information.

Animals Abortion and birth of weak offspring in cattle and goats are reported (MacDonald 1952b, Allen and Kitts 1961, Call and James 1978, Panter et al. 1987, Gartner et al. 1988, Lacey et al. 1988, Panter et al. 1988b).

POLYGONACEAE buckwheat family

Rheum rhaponticum L.
rhubarb/rhubarbe
Perennial crop plant.

Humans Poisoning and death are reported after the ingestion of large quantities of leaves (Anonymous 1917, Robb 1919, Culpepper and Moon 1933, Cooper and Johnson 1984).

Animals No information.

Rumex acetosa L.
garden-sorrel/grande oseille
Naturalized in Nfld., (P.E.I.), N.S., N.B., Que., Ont., Man., Sask., Alta., and B.C.; cultivated as salad plant.

Humans No information.

Animals Sheep were poisoned from grazing a field with a dense crop of garden-sorrel (Coward 1949).

Rumex venosus Pursh
veined dock/rumex veiné
Native herb in southern Man., Sask., and Alta.

Humans No information.

Animals Sickness and death of cattle are reported (Dickie et al. 1978).

POLYPODIACEAE fern family

Onoclea sensibilis L.
sensitive fern/onoclée sensible
Native herb in Nfld., N.S., P.E.I., N.B., Que., Ont., and Man.

Humans No information.

Animals Sickness and death of horses are reported after eating hay containing sensitive fern (Waller et al. 1944, Hodgdon 1951).

Pteridium aquilinum (L.) Kuhn
bracken/grande fougère
Native herb in Nfld., N.S., P.E.I., N.B., Que., Ont., Man., Alta., and B.C.

Humans Although sometimes eaten, recent evidence indicates that it is carcinogenic (Cody and Crompton 1975, Evans 1976, Pamucku et al. 1977, Fenwick 1988, Milne 1988).

Animals Sickness and death in cattle, horses, sheep, and pigs are reported (Hadwen 1917, Hadwen and Bruce 1933, Groh 1941, Weswig et al. 1946, Campagne 1956, Langham 1957, Wagnon 1959, Rosenberger 1971, Cody and Crompton 1975, Evans 1976, Kelleway and Geovjian 1978, Fenwick 1988, Milne 1988).

PRIMULACEAE   primrose family

Anagallis arvensis L.
scarlet pimpernel/mouron rouge
Naturalized herb in N.S., (P.E.I.), (N.B.), Que., Ont., Alta., and B.C.

Humans No information.

Animals Poisoning and sometimes death are reported of dogs, horses, mules, poultry, rabbits, wild birds, calves, and sheep after they consume large quantities of vegetation or seed (Cooper and Johnson 1984).

Primula obconica Hance.
primula
Ornamental herb.

Humans Severe dermatitis occurs in some people, from a skin-irritant in glandular hairs on flower stalks and calyx (Mitchell and Rook 1979, Frohne and Pfänder 1983, Fernandez et al. 1987).

Animals No information.

RANUNCULACEAE   crowfoot family

Aconitum napellus L.
monk's hood/aconit Napel
Outdoor ornamental herb.

Humans This herb is very poisonous if ingested, especially the root (Frohne and Pfänder 1983, Cooper and Johnson 1984, Lampe and McCann 1985).

Animals No information.

Delphinium bicolor Nutt.
low larkspur/pied d'alouette bicolore
Native herb in southwestern Sask., Alta., and B.C.

Delphinium glaucum S. Wats (= *D. brownii* Rydb.)
tall larkspur/pied d'alouette glauque
Native herb in Mackenzie Dist., Y.T., Que., Ont., Man., Sask., Alta., and B.C.

Delphinium menziesii DC.
Menzies larkspur
Native herb in B.C.

Humans No information.

Animals Reports document poisoning and death of cattle and suspected poisoning of horses and sheep (Wilcox 1897, Chesnut and Wilcox 1901, Marsh et al. 1923*a*, Marsh 1929*a*, McLean and Nicholson 1958, Nation et al. 1982, Frohne and Pfänder 1983, Cronin et al. 1988, Nielsen and Ralphs 1988).

Ranunculus bulbosus L.
bulbous buttercup/renoncule bulbeuse
Naturalized herb in Nfld., N.S., (Que.), Ont., and (B.C.).

Humans Children have been poisoned from the ingestion of bulbous plant parts (Forsyth 1968, Frohne and Pfänder 1983).

Animals No information.

RHAMNACEAE buckthorn family

Rhamnus cathartica L.
European buckthorn/nerprun commun
Small naturalized tree in N.S., P.E.I., (N.B.), Que., Ont., Man., and Sask.

Rhamnus frangula L.
alder buckthorn/nerprun bourdaine
Small naturalized shrub or tree in N.S., P.E.I., N.B., Que., Ont., and Man.

Humans Rare cases of mild poisoning are reported; buckthorns contain substances with laxative properties (Kingsbury 1964, Frohne and Pfänder 1983, Cooper and Johnson 1984).

Animals No information.

ROSACEAE rose family

Prunus serotina Ehrh.
black cherry/cerisier tardif
Native tree in N.S., P.E.I., N.B., Que., and Ont.; occasionally cultivated.

Humans Poisoning has occurred after the ingestion of seed in fruits, from chewing twigs, and from making tea from leaves (Chesnut 1898, Hardin and Arena 1974, Mulligan and Munro 1981*a*).

Animals Poisoning and death of livestock are reported (Chesnut 1898, Morse and Howard 1898, Beath et al. 1953, McLean and Nicholson 1958, Kingsbury 1964, Conn 1978, Mulligan and Munro 1981*a*).

Prunus virginiana L.
red chokecherry/cerisier de Virginie

Native shrub or small tree in Mackenzie Dist., Nfld., N.S., P.E.I., N.B., Que., Ont., Man., Sask., Alta., and B.C.

Humans Poisoning and death are reported of children who ate large quantities of fruits without removing seeds (Pardee 1847, Pijoan 1942, Kingsbury 1964, Hardin and Arena 1974, Mulligan and Munro 1981*a*).

Animals Poisoning and death of livestock are reported (Chesnut 1898, Morse and Howard 1898, Fleming et al. 1926, Fleming and Dill 1928, Reynard and Norton 1942, Hershey 1945, Beath et al. 1953, McLean and Nicholson 1958, Kingsbury 1964, Conn 1978, Mulligan and Munro 1981*a*).

RUTACEAE   rue family

Dictamnus albus L.
gas plant/dictame
Ornamental herb.

Humans Photosensitization is reported after handling plant parts, especially seed pods; reddish patches may persist on skin for weeks (Cummer and Dexter 1937, Henderson and DesGroseilliers 1984).

Animals No information.

SAXIFRAGACEAE   saxifrage family

Hydrangea macrophylla (Thunb.) Ser.
hydrangea/hortensia
Woody ornamental.

Humans Illness is reported from ingestion of leaves or roots; hand dermatitis resulted from the repeated handling of this plant by a nurseryman (O'Leary and Hyattsville 1964, Apted 1973, Der Marderosian et al. 1976, Lampe and McCann 1985, Bruynzeel 1986).

Animals No information.

SCROPHULARIACEAE   figwort family

Digitalis purpurea L.
foxglove/digitale pourpre
Naturalized herb in Nfld., N.S., Que., Ont., and B.C.; sometimes cultivated.

Humans Sickness of children is reported after ingestion of flowers, seeds, or leaves (Kingsbury 1964, Frohne and Pfänder 1983, Cooper and Johnson 1984, Lamp and McCann 1985).

Animals Poisoning of pigs, cattle, turkeys, and other animals is reported; livestock normally avoid eating foxglove (Bruce 1927, Cooper and Johnson 1984, Thomas et al. 1987).

SIMAROUBACEAE quassia family

Ailanthus altissima (Mill.) Swingle
tree-of-heaven/frêne puant
Ornamental tree.

Humans Dermatitis is reported from contact with leaves (Muenscher 1951).

Animals No information.

SOLANACEAE nightshade family

Cestrum nocturnum L.
night-blooming jessamine/jasmin de nuit
Ornamental shrub.

Humans Sickness is reported after ingestion (Morton 1958).

Animals No information.

Datura innoxia Miller
angel's trumpet/stramoine parfumée
Ornamental herb.

Datura stramonium L.
jimsonweed/stramoine commune
Naturalized herb in N.S., P.E.I., N.B., Que., Ont., Sask., and Alta.

Humans Sickness and death are reported after ingestion of plant parts (Garvin and Ruh 1923; Jennings 1935; Hughes and Clark 1939; Goldberg 1951; Stiles 1951; Mitchell and Mitchell 1955; Jacobziner and Raybin 1960, 1961b; Mikolich 1975; Levy 1976; Moore 1976; Frohne and Pfänder 1983; Lampe and McCann 1985).

Animals Poisoning and death in cattle, horses, pigs, chickens, and mules are reported (Harshberger 1920; King 1923; Hansen 1925a, 1927; Reynard and Norton 1942; Case 1955; Leipold et al. 1973; Cooper and Johnson 1984).

Hyoscyamus niger L.
black henbane/jusquiame noire
Naturalized herb in N.S., (P.E.I.), N.B., Que., Ont., Man., and (B.C.).

Humans It is poisonous when ingested but is usually avoided because of its unpleasant odor (Hocking 1947, Kürkçüoglu 1970, Spoerke et al. 1987).

Animals No information.

Nicotiana tabacum L.
tobacco/tabac
Cultivated herb.

Humans Fresh leaves are poisonous if ingested (Kingsbury 1964).

Animals Deformities are noted in offspring after sows are fed tobacco (Crowe 1969, Menges et al. 1970, Crowe and Swerczek 1974, Keeler 1988).

Physalis peruviana L.
ground-cherry/coqueret
Ornamental herb.

Humans Fruits are considered mildly poisonous (Frohne and Pfänder 1983).

Animals No information.

Solanum dulcamara L.
climbing nightshade/morelle douce-amère
Naturalized woody vine in Nfld., N.S., P.E.I., Que., Ont., Man., Alta., and B.C.

Humans Berries are mildly poisonous, but serious poisoning has occurred after large quantities were eaten (Harshberger 1920, Alexander et al. 1948, Frohne and Pfänder 1983).

Animals Poisoning of sheep and cattle is reported, but there have been no recent reports (Yates 1915, Harshberger 1920, Craig and Kehoe 1925).

Solanum nigrum L.
black nightshade/morelle noire
Naturalized herb in (Nfld.), N.S., (P.E.I.), N.B., Que., Ont., Man., Sask., Alta., and B.C.

Humans Although sometimes eaten as food, fruits (especially unripe ones) can cause serious illness (Cooper and Johnson 1984).

Animals Poisoning and death of cattle, sheep, pigs, goats, chickens, and ducks are reported (Hansen 1927, Casselbury 1939, Hubbs 1947, Ogg et al. 1981, Cooper and Johnson 1984).

Solanum pseudo-capsicum L.
Jerusalem-cherry/cerisier d'amour

Small ornamental shrub.

Humans Nausea, abdominal pains, dilation of pupils, and drowsiness are reported after eating a few fruits (Frohne and Pfänder 1983).

Animals No information.

Solanum tuberosum L.
potato/pomme de terre

Food plant.

Humans Sickness and death are reported after eating large quantities of green-skinned potatoes or green fruits containing the chemical solanine (Hansen 1925*b*, McMillan and Thompson 1979, Frohne and Pfänder 1983).

Animals Farm animals have been poisoned by eating large quantities of spoiled potatoes or potato tops (Hansen 1928*f*, Frohne and Pfänder 1983, Cooper and Johnson 1984).

TAXACEAE   yew family

Taxus spp.
yews/ifs

Native and ornamental shrubs; widely distributed.

Humans Needles and seeds (apparently not the fleshy part of berries) are toxic if ingested; poisoning is rare (Schulte 1975, Burke et al. 1979, Cooper and Johnson 1984, Lampe and McCann 1985, Feldman et al. 1987).

Animals Cattle, sheep, goats, pigs, deer, and horses have been poisoned, especially after eating fallen or cut branches (Craig and Kehoe 1925, Bruce 1927, Brown and Hull 1951, Lowe et al. 1970, Alden et al. 1977).

THYMELAEACEAE   mezereum family

Daphne cneorum L.
garland daphne/daphné camélée

Ornamental shrub.

Daphne laureola L.
spurge-laurel/auriole

Ornamental shrub.

Daphne mezereum L.
February daphne/daphné jolibois
Ornamental shrub.

Humans   Poisoning is usually mild, as few berries are eaten because of their acrid taste (Fyles 1920, Kingsbury 1961, Frohne and Pfänder 1983, Lampe and McCann 1985).

Animals   These shrubs are usually avoided by animals; pigs and a horse have died after eating berries and foliage (Cooper and Johnson 1984).

Dirca palustris L.
leatherwood/dirca des marais
Native shrub in N.B., Que., and Ont.

Humans   Some people develop a severe irritation and blistering of the skin after handling the bark (Muenscher 1951, Lampe and McCann 1985).

Animals   No information.

UMBELLIFERAE   parsley family

Cicuta douglasii (DC.) Coult. & Rose
western water-hemlock/cicutaire pourpre
Native herb in B.C.

Cicuta maculata L.
spotted water-hemlock/carotte à Moreau
Native herb in MacKenzie Dist., Y.T., N.S., P.E.I., N.B., Que., Ont., Man., Sask., Alta., and B.C.

Cicuta virosa L.
northern water-hemlock/cicutaire du Nord
Native herb in MacKenzie Dist., Y.T., and northern parts of Que., Ont., Man., Sask., Alta., and B.C.

Humans   These water-hemlocks are extremely poisonous if ingested; sickness and death are primarily the result of ingestion of rootstocks (Pammel 1921, Haggerty and Conway 1936, Frankton 1955, Kingsbury 1964, Robson 1965, Campbell 1966, Starreveld and Hope 1975, Carlton et al. 1979, Mulligan 1980*b*, Mulligan and Munro 1981*b*, Frohne and Pfänder 1983, Cooper and Johnson 1984, Frankton and Mulligan 1987, Mulligan 1987).

Animals   Poisoning and death of all classes of livestock are reported (Chesnut 1898, Fleming et al. 1920*c*, Hansen 1928*g*, Skidmore 1933,

Gress 1935, Campagne 1956, McLean and Nicholson 1958, Tucker et al. 1964, Mulligan 1980b, Mulligan and Munro 1981b, Cooper and Johnson 1984, Panter and Keeler 1988, Panter et al. 1988c).

Conium maculatum L.
poison-hemlock/ciguë maculée
Naturalized herb in N.S., Que., Ont., Sask., and B.C.

Humans Sickness and death are reported after ingestion of leaves, roots or seeds (Pammel 1919, Muenscher 1951, Kingsbury 1964, Frohne and Pfänder 1983, Cooper and Johnson 1984, Lampe and McCann 1985).

Animals Poisoning and death of all classes of livestock. Teratogenic deformities in calves have occurred (Chesnut 1898, Pammel 1919, Anonymous 1951, Keeler 1974, Hannam 1985, Panter et al. 1985, Jessup et al. 1986, Keeler 1988, Panter et al. 1988a, c, Panter and Keeler 1988).

Heracleum mantegazzianum Somm. & Lev.
giant hogweed/berce du Caucase
Naturalized herb in southcentral Ont.

Humans A rash and persistent blisters can result when handling of leaves is followed by exposure to sunlight (Anonymous 1970, Drever and Hunter 1970, Morton 1975, Gunby 1980).

Animals No information.

Pastinaca sativa L.
wild parsnip/panais sauvage
Naturalized herb in Y.T., Nfld., N.S., P.E.I., N.B., Que., Ont., Man., Sask., Alta., and B.C.

Humans Some people develop a dermatitis after handling leaves, flowers, or fruits (Muenscher 1951, Campagne 1949, Hardin and Arena 1974).

Animals No information.

URTICACEAE   nettle family

Laportea canadensis (L.) Gaud.
Canada nettle/laportéa du Canada
Native herb in N.S., N.B., Que., Ont., and Sask.

Humans Toxic liquid in hairs causes intense itching and pain (McIntosh 1980).

Animals No information.

Urtica dioica L.
American stinging nettle/ortie dioïque d'Amérique

Native herb in Mackenzie Dist., Y.T., Lab., Nfld., N.S., P.E.I., N.B., Que., Ont., Man., Sask., Alta., and B.C.

Humans Toxic liquid in hairs causes intense itching and pain (Willis 1969, Bassett et al. 1977, McIntosh 1980).

Animals No information.

VITACEAE   grape family

Parthenocissus quinquefolia (L.) Planch.
Virginia creeper/vigne vierge

Native climbing vine in (N.S.), N.B., P.E.I., Que., Ont., and Man.

Humans Ingestion of large quantities of berries is suspected of causing serious poisoning; leaves contain raphides that cause skin irritations in some individuals (Warren 1912, Kingsbury 1961, Frohne and Pfänder 1983, Lamp and McCann 1985).

Animals No information.

APPENDIX 1. CANADIAN PLANTS POISONOUS TO HUMANS

Abrus precatorius	precatory-pea/abrus à chapelet
Aconitum napellus	monk's hood/aconit Napel
Aesculus hippocastanum (large quantities)	horse-chestnut/marronnier
Ailanthus altissima	tree-of-heaven/frêne puant
Allamanda cathartica	golden-trumpet/trompette dorée
Allium canadense	wild onion/ail du Canada
A. cepa (rare dermatitis)	onion/oignon
Aloe spp.	aloes/aloès
Amaryllis belladonna	amaryllis
A. vittata	amaryllis
Anthurium spp.	anthuriums
Apocynum androsaemifolium	spreading dogbane/apocyn à feuilles d'androsème
A. cannabinum	hemp dogbane/apocyn chanvrin
Arisaema triphyllum	Jack-in-the-pulpit/petit-prêcheur
Asarum canadense	wild ginger/asaret du Canada
Asimina triloba	pawpaw/asiminier trilobé
Baptisia leucantha	wild false indigo/baptisie leucanthe
Baptisia tinctoria	wild indigo/indigo sauvage
Caladium bicolor	caladium
Calla palustris	wild calla/calla des marais
Caulophyllum thalictroides	blue cohosh/graines à chapelet
Cestrum nocturnum	night-blooming jessamine/jasmin de nuit
Chelidonium majus	greater celandine/grande chélidoine
Chenopodium album (large quantities)	lamb's-quarters/chénopode blanc
Chrysanthemum spp.	chrysanthemums/ chrysanthèmes
Cicuta douglasii	western water-hemlock/ cicutaire pourpre
C. maculata	spotted water-hemlock/carotte à Moreau
C. virosa	northern water-hemlock/ cicutaire du Nord
Clivia spp.	Kaffir lilies/clivies
Codiaeum variegatum	croton/croton ou codier
Colchicum autumnale	autumn crocus/colchique d'automne
Conium maculatum	poison hemlock/ciguë maculée
Convallaria majalis	lily-of-the-valley/muguet
Cypripedium acaule	pink lady's-slipper/cypripède acaule

C. calceolus	yellow lady's-slipper/cypripède soulier
C. reginae	showy lady's-slipper/cypripède royal
Daphne cneorum	garland daphne/daphné camélée
D. laureola	spurge-laurel/auriole
D. mezereum	February daphne/daphné jolibois
Datura innoxia	angel's trumpet/stramoine parfumée
D. stramonium	jimsonweed/stramoine commune
Dictamnus albus	gas plant/dictame
Dieffenbachia amoena	giant dumbcane/arum vénéneux
D. bausei	dumbcane/dieffenbachia
D. picta	spotted dumbcane/dieffenbachia tachetée
Digitalis purpurea	foxglove/digitale pourpre
Dirca palustris	leatherwood/dirca des marais
Echium vulgare	blueweed/vipérine
Euonymus atropurpureus (mild symptoms)	burning bush/fusain
E. europaeus (mild symptoms)	European spindletree/fusain d'Europe
Eupatorium rugosum	white snakeroot/eupatoire rugueuse
Euphorbia cyparissias L.	cypress spurge/euphorbe cyprès
E. esula	leafy spurge/euphorbe ésule
E. helioscopia	sun spurge/euphorbe réveille-matin
E. lactea	candelabra-cactus/cactus candélabre
E. lathyris	caper spurge/cagarrino
E. milii	crown-of-thorns/couronne d'épines
E. peplus	petty spurge/euphorbe des jardins
E. tirucalli	penciltree/euphorbe effilée
Galanthus nivalis	snowdrop/perce-neige
Ginkgo biloba	maidenhair tree/ginkgo
Gloriosa superba	glory lily/glorieuse du Malabar
Gymnocladus dioicus (weak evidence)	Kentucky coffeetree/chicot du Canada
Hedera helix	English ivy/lierre commun
Heliotropium curassavicum	spatulate-leaved heliotrope/héliotrope obové de Curaçao
Heracleum mantegazzianum	giant hogweed/berce du Caucase
Hydrangea macrophylla	hydrangea/hortensia
Hyoscyamus niger	black henbane/jusquiame noire
Ilex opaca (weak evidence)	American holly/houx d'Amérique
Iva xanthifolia	false ragweed/fausse herbe à poux
Kochia scoparia	kochia/kochia à balais
Laburnum anagyroides	golden-chain/cytise

Laportea canadensis	Canada nettle/laportéa du Canada
Lathyrus odoratus (over long period)	sweet pea/pois de senteur
L. sativus (over long period)	grass pea/lentille d'Espagne
Leonurus cardiaca	motherwort/agripaume cardiaque
Ligustrum vulgare	common privet/troène commun
Lobelia cardinalis	cardinalflower/lobélie du cardinal
L. inflata	Indian-tobacco/lobélie gonflée
L. siphilitica	blue cardinalflower/cardinale bleue
Lonicera spp. (mild symptoms)	honeysuckles/chèvrefeuilles
Lupinus spp.	lupines/lupins
Maclura pomifera	osage-orange/bois d'arc
Menispermum canadense	moonseed/ménisperme du Canada
Monstera deliciosa	Swiss-cheese plant/ philodendron monstéra
Narcissus poeticus	narcissus/narcisse
N. pseudonarcissus	daffodil/jonquille
Nerium oleander	oleander/laurier rose
Nicotiana tabacum L.	tobacco/tabac
Ornithogalum umbellatum	star-of-Bethlehem/dame d'onze heures
Papaver nudicaulis	Iceland poppy/pavot d'Islande
P. orientale	oriental poppy/pavot d'Orient
P. rhoeas	corn poppy/pavot coquelicot
P. somniferum	opium poppy/pavot somnifère
Parthenocissus quinquefolia	Virginia creeper/vigne vierge
Pastinaca sativa	wild parsnip/panais sauvage
Phacelia campanularia	California bluebell/phacélie de Californie
Philodendron spp.	philodendrons
Phoradendron flavescens (mild symptoms)	American mistletoe/gui de chêne
Physalis peruviana	ground-cherry/coqueret
Phytolacca americana	pokeweed/phytolaque d'Amérique
Podophyllum peltatum	May-apple/podophylle pelté
Primula obconica	primula
Prunus serotina	black cherry/cerisier tardif
P. virginiana	red chokecherry/cerisier de Virginie
Pteridium aquilinum	bracken/grande fougère
Ranunculus bulbosus	bulbous buttercup/renoncule bulbeuse
Rhamnus cathartica	European buckthorn/nerprun commun
R. frangula	alder buckthorn/nerprun bourdaine

Rheum rhaponticum (leaf blades)	rhubarb/rhubarbe
Rhododendron albiflorum	white rose-bay/azalée blanche
R. macrophyllum	California rose-bay/rhododendron de Californie
Rhododendron spp.	azaleas/rhododendrons
Rhus diversiloba	western poison-oak/sumac de l'Ouest
R. radicans	poison-ivy/herbe à la puce
R. vernix	poison sumac/sumac à vernis
Ricinus communis	castor bean/ricin
Robinia pseudoacacia	black locust/robinier
Sambucus spp. (mild symptoms)	elders/sureaux
Senecio jacobaea	tansy ragwort/séneçon jacobée
Solanum dulcamara	climbing nightshade/morelle douce-amère
S. nigrum	black nightshade/morelle noire
S. pseudo-capsicum	Jerusalem-cherry/cerisier d'amour
S. tuberosum (green)	potato/pomme de terre
Symphoricarpos albus (mild symptoms)	thin-leaved snowberry/ symphorine à grappes
Symplocarpus foetidus	skunk cabbage/chou puant
Taxus spp.	yews/ifs
Thermopsis rhombifolia	golden-bean
Tulipa spp. (prolonged contact)	tulips/tulipes
Urtica dioica	American stinging nettle/ortie dioïque d'Amérique
Veratrum viride	false hellebore/varaire vert
Viburnum opulus (mild symptoms)	Guelder-rose/obier
Wisteria spp.	wisterias/glycines
Zigadenus elegans	white camas/zigadène élégant
Z. gramineus	death camas/zigadène vénéneux

APPENDIX 2. CANADIAN PLANTS POISONOUS TO ANIMALS

Acer rubrum	red maple/érable rouge
Aesculus hippocastanum	horse-chestnut/marronnier
Agrostemma githago	purple cockle/nielle
Allium cepa	onion/oignon
Amaranthus blitoides	prostrate pigweed/amarante fausse-blite
A. hybridus	smooth pigweed/amarante hybride
A. retroflexus	redroot pigweed/amarante à racine rouge
Amsinkia intermedia	fiddleneck
Anagallis arvensis	scarlet pimpernel/mouron rouge
Apocynum androsaemifolium	spreading dogbane/apocyn à feuilles d'androsème
A. cannabinum	hemp dogbane/apocyn chanvrin
Asclepias speciosa	showy milkweed/belle asclépiade
A. syriaca	common milkweed/asclépiade de Syrie
A. verticillata	eastern whorled milkweed/asclépiade verticillée
Astragalus bisulcatus	two-grooved milk-vetch/ astragale fondu
A. lentiginosus	
A. miser	timber milk-vetch/astragale prostré
Barbarea vulgaris	yellow rocket/barbarée vulgaire
Bassia hyssopifolia	five-hooked bassia/bassia à feuilles d'hysope
Centaurea solstitialis	yellow star-thistle/centaurée du solstice
Chenopodium album	lamb's-quarters/chénopode blanc
Chrysothamnus nauseosus	stinking rabbitbush/bigelovie puante
Cicuta douglasii	western water-hemlock/ cicutaire pourpre
C. maculata	spotted water-hemlock/carotte à Moreau
C. virosa	northern water-hemlock/ cicutaire du Nord
Conium maculatum	poison-hemlock/ciguë maculée
Cynoglossum officinale	hound's-tongue/cynoglosse officinal
Daphne cneorum	garland daphne/daphné camélée
D. laureola	spurge-laurel/auriole
D. mezereum	February daphne/daphné jolibois

Datura innoxia	angel's trumpet/stramoine parfumée
D. stramonium	jimsonweed/stramoine commune
Delphinium bicolor	low larkspur/pied d'alouette bicolore
D. glaucum	tall larkspur/pied d'alouette glauque
D. menziesii	Menzies larkspur
Descurainia pinnata	green tansy mustard/moutarde tanaisie verte
Dicentra canadensis	squirrel-corn/dicentre du Canada
D. cucullaria	Dutchman's-breeches/dicentre à capuchon
D. formosa	western bleedingheart/diélytra à belles fleurs
Digitalis purpurea	foxglove/digitale pourpre
Equisetum arvense	field horsetail/prêle des champs
E. palustre	marsh horsetail/prêle des marais
Eupatorium rugosum	white snakeroot/eupatoire rugueuse
Euphorbia cyparissias	cypress spurge/euphorbe cyprès
E. esula	leafy spurge/euphorbe ésule
Glechoma hederacea	ground-ivy/lierre terrestre
Glyceria grandis	tall manna grass/glycérie géante
Gutierrezia sarothrae	broom snakeweed/gutierrezie faux-sarothra
Helenium autumnale	sneezeweed/hélénie automnale
H. flexuosum	naked-flowered sneezeweed/hélénie nudiflore
Hymenoxys richardsonii	Colorado rubberweed/hyménoxys de Richardson
Hypericum perforatum	St. John's-wort/millepertuis perforé
Iris versicolor	blue flag/clajeux
Kalmia angustifolia	sheep-laurel/kalmia à feuilles étroites
K. polifolia	bog-laurel/kalmia à feuilles d'andromède
Kochia scoparia	kochia/kochia à balais
Lactuca scariola	prickly lettuce/laitue scariole
Lathyrus odoratus	sweet pea/pois de senteur
L. sativus	grass pea/lentille d'Espagne
Lupinus argenteus	silvery lupine/lupin argenté
L. burkei	Burke's lupine
L. polyphyllus	large-leaved lupine/lupin polyphylle
L. pusillus	small lupine
L. sericeus	silky lupine/lupin soyeux

Menziesia ferruginea	western minniebush/menziézie ferrugineuse
Nicotiana tabacum	tobacco/tabac
Onoclea sensibilis	sensitive fern/onoclée sensible
Oxytropis lambertii	purple locoweed/oxytrope de Lambert
O. sericea	locoweed/oxytrope
Phytolacca americana	pokeweed/phytolaque d'Amérique
Pinus ponderosa	ponderosa pine/pin ponderosa
Podophyllum peltatum	May-apple/podophylle pelté
Prunus serotina	black cherry/cerisier tardif
P. virginiana	red chokecherry/cerisier de Virginie
Pteridium aquilinum	bracken/grande fougère
Quercus rubra	red oak/chêne rouge
Q. velutina	black oak/chêne noir
Rhododendron albiflorum	white rose-bay/azalée blanche
R. macrophyllum	California rose-bay/rhododendron de Californie
Robinia pseudoacacia	black locust/robinier
Rudbeckia laciniata	cut-leaved coneflower/rudbeckie laciniée
R. serotina	black-eyed Susan/rudbeckie hérissée
Rumex acetosa	garden sorrel/grande oseille
R. venosus	veined dock/rumex veiné
Sarcobatus vermiculatus	greasewood/sarcobatus vermiculé
Senecio jacobaea	tansy ragwort/séneçon jacobée
S. vulgaris	common groundsel/séneçon vulgaire
Sinapis arvensis	wild mustard/moutarde des champs
Solanum dulcamara	climbing nightshade/morelle douce-amère
S. nigrum	black nightshade/morelle noire
S. tuberosum	potato/pomme de terre
Solidago mollis	velvety goldenrod/verge d'or veloutée
Suckleya suckleyana	poison suckleya/suckleya
Taxus spp.	yews/ifs
Thermopsis rhombifolia	golden-bean
Thlaspi arvense	stinkweed/tabouret des champs
Triglochin maritima	seaside arrow-grass/troscart maritime
Veratrum viride	false hellebore/varaire vert
Vicia villosa	hairy vetch/vesce velue
Xanthium strumarium	cocklebur/lampourde glouteron
Zigadenus elegans	white camas/zigadène élégant
Z. gramineus	death camas/zigadène vénéneux

BIBLIOGRAPHY

Aanes, W.A. 1961. Pingue (*Hymenoxys richardsonii*) poisoning in sheep. Am. J. Vet. Res. 22:47–51.

Agriculture Alberta. 1983. Outdoor plants. Harmful or poisonous to humans. Edmonton Agdex 666-2. 29 pp.

Agriculture Québec. 1975. Noms des maladies des plantes du Canada/Names of plant diseases in Canada. Quebec City, Publ. QA38-R4-1. 288 pp.

Alden, C.L.; Fosnaugh, C.J.; Smith, J.B.; Mohan, R. 1977. Japanese yew poisoning of large domestic animals in the midwest. J. Am. Vet. Med. Assoc. 170:314–316.

Alex, J.F.; Cayouette, R.; Mulligan, G.A. 1980. Common and botanical names of weeds in Canada/Noms populaires et scientifiques des plantes nuisibles du Canada. Agric. Can. Publ. 1397. Revised. 132 pp.

Alexander, R.F.; Forbes, G.B.; Hawkins, E.S. 1948. A fatal case of solanine poisoning. Br. Med. J. 2:518.

Allen, M.R.; Kitts, W.D. 1961. The effect of yellow pine (*Pinus ponderosa*) needles on the reproductivity of the laboratory female mouse. Can. J. Anim. Sci. 41:1–8.

Angunawela, R.M.; Fernando, H.A. 1971. Acute ascending polyneuropathy and dermatitis following poisoning by tubers of *Gloriosa superba*. Ceylon Med. J. Dec.:233–235.

Anonymous. 1874. A poisonous composite plant. Pharm. J. 4:518.

Anonymous. 1917. The danger of eating rhubarb leaves. Sci. Am. 117:82.

Anonymous. 1951. Unusual case of hemlock poisoning in swine. Calif. Vet. 5:26.

Anonymous. 1961. Wisteria. Natl. Clearinghouse Poison Control Cent. Bull. July–Aug. 1–2.

Anonymous. 1970. The giant hogweed. Lancet 2:32.

Anonymous. 1972. Beware—poisonous plant. The Daily News (Newspaper), Nelson, B.C. 71(No. 99):2.

Apted, J.H. 1973. Phytodermatitis from hydrangeas. Arch. Dermatol. 108:427.

Arditti, J.; Rodriguez, E. 1982. *Dieffenbachia*: Uses, abuses and toxic constituents: A review. J. Ethnopharmacol. 5:293–302.

Ayres, S., Jr.; Ayres, S., III. 1958. Philodendron as a cause of contact dermatitis. Arch. Dermatol. 78:330–333.

Baer, H. 1983. Allergic contact dermatitis from plants. Pages 421–442 *in* Keeler, R.F.; Tu, A.T., eds. Handbook of natural toxins. Vol. 1. Plant and fungal toxins. Marcel Dekker Inc., New York, N.Y.

Bandeline, F.J.; Malesh, W. 1956. Alkaloids of *Chelidonium majus* L., leaves and stems. I. J. Am. Pharm. Assoc. Sci. Ed. 45:702.

Barber, M.A. 1905. Poisoning due to the pawpaw (*Asimina triloba*). J. Am. Med. Assoc. 45:2013.

Barnes, M.F. 1921. Black locust poisoning of chickens. J. Am. Vet. Med. Assoc. 59:370–372.

Barnes, M.F.; Fox, L.E. 1955. Poisoning with *Dieffenbachia*. J. Hist. Med. Allied Sci. 10:173.

Barnett, B.D. 1975. Toxicity of pokeberries (fruit of *Phytolacca americana* L.) for turkey poults. Poult. Sci. 54:1215–1217.

Bassett, I.J.; Crompton, C.W. 1978. The biology of Canadian weeds. 32. *Chenopodium album* L. Can. J. Plant Sci. 58:1061–1072.

Bassett, I.J.; Crompton, C.W.; Parmelee, J.A. 1978. An atlas of airborne pollen grains and common fungus spores of Canada. Agric. Can. Monogr. 18. 321 pp.

Bassett, I.J.; Crompton, C.W.; Woodland, D.W. 1977. The biology of Canadian weeds. 21. *Urtica dioica* L. Can. J. Plant Sci. 57:491–498.

Beath, O.A. 1920. The chemical examination of the silvery lupine. Univ. Wyo. Agric. Exp. Stn. Bull. 125:101–114.

Beath, O.A. 1925. Lupine studies II. The silvery lupine. Univ. Wyo. Agric. Exp. Stn. Bull. 144. 16 pp.

Beath, O.A.; Draize, J.H.; Eppson, H.F. 1932. Three poisonous vetches. Univ. Wyo. Agric. Exp. Stn. Bull. 189. 23 pp.

Beath, O.A.; Draize, J.H.; Eppson, H.F. 1933. Arrow grass—chemical and physiological considerations. Univ. Wyo. Agric. Exp. Stn. Bull. 193. 36 pp.

Beath, O.A.; Gilbert, C.S.; Eppson, H.F.; Rosenfeld, I. 1953. Poisonous plants and livestock poisoning. Wyo. Agric. Exp. Stn. Bull. 324. 94 pp.

Beath, O.A.; Lehnert, E.H. 1917. The poisonous properties of the two-grooved milk vetch (*Astragalus bisulcatus*). Univ. Wyo. Agric. Exp. Stn. Bull. 112:59–67.

Berry, T.J.; Gonzales, P. 1986. Do your cattle-owning clients know about this poisonous range plant. Vet. Med. 81:1055–1056.

Black, O.F.; Eggleston, W.W.; Kelly, J.W. 1930. Toxicity of *Bikukulla formosa* (western bleeding heart). J. Agric. Res. 40:917–920.

Black, O.F.; Eggleston, W.W.; Kelly, J.W.; Turner, H.C. 1923. Poisonous properties of *Bikukulla cucullaria* (Dutchman's-breeches) and *B. canadensis* (squirrel-corn). J. Agric. Res. 23:69–78.

Boivin, B. 1948. Centurie de plantes canadiennes. Nat. Can. 75:202–227.

Boivin, B. 1966, 1967. Énumération des plantes du Canada. Provancheria 6. Nat. Can. 93:253–274, 371–437, 583–646, 989–1063; 94:131–157, 471–528, 625–655.

Boudreault, M. 1979. Guide pratique des plantes médicinales du Québec. Marcel Broquet Inc., La Prairie, Québec. 205 pp.

Boyle, J.; Harman, R.M.H. 1985. Contact dermatitis to *Hedera helix* (common ivy). Contact Dermatitis 12:111–112.

Brown,R.G.; Hull, F.E. 1951. *Taxus* (yew) poisoning in cattle. J. Am. Vet. Med. Assoc. 118:398–399.

Bruce, E.A. 1927. *Astragalus campestris* and other stock poisoning plants of British Columbia. Agric. Can. Bull. 88. 44 pp.

Bruynzeel, D.P. 1986. Allergic contact dermatitis to hydrangea. Contact Dermatitis 14:128.

Buck, W.M.; Preston, K.S.; Abel, M; Marshall, M.S. 1966. Perirenal edema in swine: A disease caused by common weeds. J. Am. Vet. Med. Assoc. 148:1525–1531.

Burke, M.J.; Siegel, D.; Davidow, B. 1979. Consequence of yew (*Taxus*) needle ingestion. N.Y. State J. Med. 79:1576–1577.

Call, J.W.; James, L.F. 1978. Pine needle abortion in cattle. Pages 587–590 *in* Keeler, R.F., et al., eds. Effects of poisonous plants on livestock, Academic Press, New York, N.Y.

Cameron, K. 1952. Death camas poisoning. Northwest Med. 1952:682–683.

Campagne, E. 1949. Plantes causant la fievre des foins et des dermatites dans l'est du Québec. Agric. (Qué.) 6:132–142.

Campagne, E. 1956. Plantes vénéneuses des pâturages et des récoltes. La Ferme 17:1–10.

Campbell, E.W. 1966. Plant poisoning Umbelliferae (parsley family). J. Maine Med. Assoc. 57:40–42.

Campbell, J.B.; Lodge, R.W.; Budd, A.C. 1956. Poisonous plants of the Canadian prairies. Agric. Can. Publ. 900. Revised. 31 pp.

Cann, H.M.; Verhulst, H.L. 1959. Toxic hazards at Christmas. Natl. Clearinghouse Poison Control Cent. Bull. Dec.:1.

Carlton, B.E.; Tufts, E.D.; Girard, D.E. 1979. Water hemlock poisoning complicated by rhabdomyolysis and renal failure. Clin. Toxicol. 14:87–92.

Case, A.A. 1954. Shepherd's clinic. Sheep Breeder 74:9–11.

Case, A.A. 1955. Nightshade poisoning. Southwest. Vet. 9:140–143.

Case, A.A. 1957. Some aspects of nitrate intoxication in livestock. J. Am. Vet. Med. Assoc. 130:323–329.

Casselberry, N.H. 1939. Nightshade poisoning of swine. Vet. Med. 34:444–445.

Chesnut, V.K. 1898. Thirty poisonous plants of the United States. U.S. Dep. Agric. Farmer's Bull. 86. 60 pp.

Chesnut, V.K.; Wilcox, E.V. 1901. The stock-poisoning plants of Montana. U.S. Dep. Agric. Div. Bot. Bull. 26. 150 pp.

Clark, J.G. 1979. Whorled milkweed poisoning. Vet. Hum. Toxicol. 21:431.

Claughton, W.P.; Claughton, H.D. 1954. Vetch seed poisoning. Auburn Vet. 10:125–126.

Clawson, A.B. 1933a. The American groundsels, species of *Senecio* as stock poisoning plants. Vet. Med. 28:105–110.

Clawson, A.B. 1933b. Alpine kalmia (*Kalmia microphylla*) as a stock-poisoning plant. U.S. Dep. Agric. Tech. Bull. 391. 10 pp.

Clawson, A.B.; Moran, E.A. 1937. Toxicity of arrowgrass for sheep and remedial treatment. U.S. Dep. Agric. Tech. Bull. 580. 16 pp.

Cody, W.J.; Crompton, C.W. 1975. The biology of Canadian weeds. 15. *Pteridium aquilinum* (L.) Kuhn. Can. J. Plant Sci. 55:1059–1072.

Cody, W.J.; Wagner, W. 1981. The biology of Canadian weeds. 49. *Equisetum arvense* L. Can. J. Plant Sci. 61:123–133.

Concalo, S.; Freitas, J.D.; Sousa, I. 1987. Contact dermatitis from *Narcissus-pseudonarcissus*. Contact Dermatitis 16:115–116.

Conn, E.E. 1978. Cyanogenesis, the production of hydrogen cyanide by plants. Pages 301–310 in Keeler, R.F., et al., eds. Effects of poisonous plants on livestock. Academic Press, New York, N.Y.

Cooper, M.S.; Johnson, A.W. 1984. Poisonous plants in Britain. Min. Agric. Food Ref. Book 161. Her Majesty's Stationery Office, London. 305 pp.

Cordy, D.R. 1954. Nigropallidal encephalomalacia in horses associated with ingestion of yellow star thistle. J. Neuropathol. Exp. Neurol. 13:330–342.

Couch, J.F. 1922. The toxic constituent of greasewood (*Sarcobatus vermiculatus*). Am. J. Pharm. 94:631–641.

Couch, J.F. 1926a. Acidosis, trembles and milksickness. Science 64:456–457.

Couch, J.F. 1926b. Relative toxicity of the lupine alkaloids. J. Agric. Res. 32:51–67.

Couch, J.F. 1927. The toxic constituent of richweed or white snakeroot (*Eupatorium urticaefolium*). J. Agric. Res. 35:547–576.

Couch, J.F. 1933. Trembles (or milksickness). U.S. Dep. Agric. Circ. 306. 12 pp.

Coward, T.G. 1949. Acute, fatal poisoning in sheep due to the ingestion of common sorrel (*Rumex acetosa*). Vet. Rec. 46:765–766.

Craig, J.F.; Kehoe, D. 1925. Plant poisoning. Vet. Rec. 38:793–825.

Crompton, C.W.; Hall, I.V.; Jensen, K.I.N.; Hildebrand, P.D. 1988. The biology of Canadian weeds. 83. *Hypericum perforatum* L. Can. J. Plant Sci. 68:149–162.

Cronin, E.H.; Olsen, J.D.; Laycock, W.A. 1988. Ecological considerations of the larkspurs. Pages 107–118 *in* James, L.F., et al., eds. The ecology and economic impact of poisonous plants on livestock production. Westview Press, Boulder, Colo.

Crowe, M.W. 1969. Skeletal anomalies in pigs associated with tobacco. Mod. Vet. Pract. 69:54.

Crowe, M.W.; Swerczek, T.W. 1974. Congenital arthrogryposis in offspring of sows fed tobacco (*Nicotiana tabacum*). Am. J. Vet. Res. 35:1071.

Culpepper, C.W.; Moon, H.H. 1933. Composition of rhubarb at different stages of maturity in relation to its use in cooking and canning. J. Agric. Res. 46:387–402.

Cummer, C.L.; Dexter, R. 1937. Dermatitis caused by *Dictamnus albus* (gas plant), an example of photosensitization. J. Am. Med. Assoc. 109:495–497.

Davis, A.M.; Stout, D.M. 1986. Anagyrin in western American lupines. Range Manage. 39:29–30.

Davis, J.H. 1978. *Abrus precatorius* (Rosary Pea): The most common lethal plant poison. J. Fla. Med. Assoc. 65:189–191.

Der Marderosian, A.; Giller, F.; Roia, F., Jr. 1976. Phytochemical and toxicological screenings of household plants potentially toxic to humans. I. J. Toxicol. Environ. Health 1:939–953.

Dickie, C.W.; Berryman, J.R. 1979. Polioencephalomalacia and photosensitization associated with *Kochia scoparia* consumption in range cattle. J. Am. Vet. Med. Assoc. 175:463–465.

Dickie, C.W.; Hamann, M.H.; Carroll, W.D.; Chow, F. 1978. Oxalate (*Rumex venosus*) poisoning in cattle. J. Am. Vet. Med. Assoc. 173:73–78.

Dickie, C.W.; James, L.F. 1983. *Kochia scoparia* poisoning in cattle. J. Am. Vet. Med. Assoc. 183:765–768.

Divers, T.J.; George, L.W.; George, J.W. 1982. Hemolytic anemia in horses after the ingestion of red maple leaves. J. Am. Vet. Med. Assoc. 180:300–302.

Donald, L.G.; Shanks, P.L. 1956. Ragwort poisoning from silage. Br. Vet. J. 112:307–311.

Dorsey, C. 1958. Philodendron dermatitis. Calif. Med. 88:329–330.

Doyle, L.P.; Walkey, F.L. 1949. White snakeroot. Poisoning in livestock. Revised. Purdue Univ. Indiana Agric. Exp. Stn. S.B. 270. 14 pp.

Drever, J.C.; Hunter, J.A.A. 1970. Hazards of giant hogweed. Br. Med. J. 3:109.

Duckworth, R.H. 1975. Poisoning of cattle by *Amaranthus*. N.Z. Vet. J. 23:154–155.

Duncan, C.S. 1961. Oak leaf poisoning in two horses. Cornell Vet. 51:159–162.

Elissalde, M.H.; Ivie, G.W. 1987. Inhibition of macrophage adenylate cyclase by the α-methylene-γ-lactone moiety of sesquiterpene lactones from forage plants. Am. J. Vet. Res. 48:148–152.

Ellis, L.C.; James, L.F.; McMullen, R.W.; Panter, K.E. 1985. Reduced progesterone and altered cotyledonary prostaglandin values induced by locoweed (*Astragalus lentiginosus*) in sheep. Am. J. Vet. Res. 46:1903–1907.

Emery, Z.T. 1887. Report of thirty-two cases of poisoning by locust bark. N.Y. State J. Med. 45:92.

Epstein, W.L. 1958. *Rhus* dermatitis: Fact and fiction. Kaiser Foundation Med. Bull. 6:197–204.

Epstein, W.L.; Byers, V.S. 1981. Poison oak and poison ivy dermatitis. Prevention and treatment in forest service work. U.S. Dep. Agric. For. Serv. 14 pp.

Evans, W.C. 1976. Bracken thiaminase-mediated neurotoxic syndromes. J. Bot. Linn. Soc. 73:113–131.

Feldman, R.; Szajewski, J.M.; Chrobak, J.; Liberek, Z.M. 1987. Four cases of self-poisoning with yew leaves decoction. Vet. Hum. Toxicol. 29:72.

Fenwick, G.R. 1988. Bracken (*Pteridium aquilinum*)—Toxic effects and toxic constituents. J. Sci. Food Agric. 46:147–173.

Fernandez, D.I.; Leanizbarrutia, I.; Munoz, D.; Bernaola, G.; Fernandez, E. 1987. Contact dermatitis from a neighbour's *Primula*. Contact Dermatitis 16:234–235.

Fleming, C.E. 1920. Poisonous range plants. Nev. Agric. Exp. Stn. Annu. Rep. 1913:39–43.

Fleming, C.E.; Dill, R. 1928. The poisoning of sheep on mountain grazing ranges in Nevada by western chokecherry (*Prunus demissa*). Univ. Nev. Agric. Exp. Stn. Bull. 110. 14 pp.

Fleming, C.E.; Miller, M.R.; Vawter, L.R. 1926. The common choke-cherry as a poisonous plant to sheep and cattle. Univ. Nev. Agric. Exp. Stn. Bull. 109. 30 pp.

Fleming, C.E.; Miller, M.R.; Vawter, L.R. 1928. The greasewood (*Sarcobatus vermiculatus*). A range plant poisonous to sheep. Univ. Nev. Agric. Exp. Stn. Bull. 115. 22 pp.

Fleming, C.E.; Peterson, N.F.; Miller, M.R.; Vawter, L.R.; Wright, L.H. 1920a. The narrow-leaved milkweed (*Asclepias mexicana*) and the broad-leaved or showy milkweed (*Asclepias speciosa*)— Plants poisonous to livestock in Nevada. Nev. Agric. Exp. Stn. Bull. 99. 32 pp.

Fleming, C.E.; Peterson, N.F.; Miller, M.R.; Wright, L.H. 1921. Death camas (*Zygadenus paniculatus* and *Zygadenus venenosus*). Plants poisonous to sheep and cattle. Univ. Nev. Agric. Exp. Stn. Bull. 101. 31 pp.

Fleming, C.E.; Peterson, N.F.; Miller, M.R.; Wright, L.H.; Louck, R.C. 1920b. Arrowgrass, a new stock-poisoning plant. Nev. Agric. Exp. Stn. Bull. 98. 21 pp.

Fleming, C.E.; Peterson, N.F.; Miller, M.R.; Wright, L.H.; Louck, R.C. 1920c. The poison parsnip or water hemlock. Nev. Agric. Exp. Stn. Bull. 100. 23 pp.

Fleming, C.E.; Schappelle, B.F. 1918. Range plants poisonous to sheep and cattle in Nevada. Univ. Nev. Agric. Exp. Stn. Bull. 95. 37 pp.

Fleurbec. 1978. Plantes sauvages des villes et des champs, vol. 1. Fleurbec & Editeur officiel du Québec, Qué. 273 pp.

Fleurbec. 1981. Plantes sauvages comestibles. Fleurbec, Saint-Cuthbert, Qué. 167 pp.

Fleurbec. 1983. Plantes sauvages des villes, des champs et en bordure des chemins, vol. 2. Fleurbec & Québec Science, Saint-Augustin, Qué. 208 pp.

Fleurbec. 1987. Plantes sauvages des lacs, rivières et tourbières. Fleurbec & Québec Science, Saint-Augustin, Qué. 397 pp.

Forrest, G.P. 1938. Cocklebur poisoning. J. Am. Vet. Med. Assoc. 93:42–43.

Forsyth, A.A. 1968. British poisonous plants. Min. Agric. Fish. Food London Bull. 161. 131 pp.

Frankton, C. 1955. (Information on a herbarium sheet of *Cicuta douglasii* in the Canada Department of Agriculture, Ottawa, Ont.).

Frankton, C.; Mulligan, G.A. 1987. Weeds of Canada. Revised. N.C. Press, Toronto, Ont. 217 pp.

French, C. 1900. Pokeroot poisoning. N.Y. State J. Med. 72:653–654.

Frohne, D.; Pfänder, H.J. 1983. A colour atlas of poisonous plants. Wolfe Publ. Ltd., London. 291 pp. [Translated from German.]

Fyles, F. 1920. Principal poisonous plants of Canada. Agric. Can. Exp. Farms Bull. 39 (2nd Ser.). 120 pp.

Gaillard, G.E. 1956. The modern treatment of poison ivy. N.Y. State J. Med. 56:2255–2259.

Galitzer, S.J.; Oehme, F.W. 1978. *Kochia scoparia* (L.) Schrad. toxicity in cattle: A literature review. Vet. Hum. Toxicol. 20:421–423.

Gardiner, W.W. 1903. Locust-tree bark poisoning. Am. Vet. Rev. 27:599–600.

Gartner, F.R.; Johnson, F.D.; Morgan, P. 1988. Cattle abortion from ponderosa pine needles: Ecological and range management considerations. Pages 71–93 *in* James, L.F., et al., eds. The ecology and economic impact of poisonous plants on livestock production. Westview Press, Boulder, Colo.

Garvin, J.A.; Ruh, H.O. 1923. Acute poisoning due to eating the seeds of jimson weed (*Datura stramonium*). Arch. Pediatr. 40:827–831.

Gilbert, C.S.; Eppson, H.F.; Bradley, W.B.; Beath, O.A. 1946. Nitrate accumulation in cultivated plants and weeds. Univ. Wyo. Agric. Exp. Stn. Bull. 277. 39 pp.

Gilfillan, F.A.; Otsuki, C. 1938. Toxicity in the leaves of *Rhododendron californica* Hook. J. Am. Pharm. Assoc. Sci. 27:396–400.

Gillett, J.M.; Robson, N.K.B. 1981. The St. John's-worts of Canada (Guttiferae). Nat. Mus. Nat. Sci. (Ott.) Publ. Bot. 11. 40 pp.

Goldberg, R.E. 1951. The jimson weed menace. Today's Health 29:38–39, 66.

Goldman, L.; Preston, R.H.; Muegel, H.R. 1956. Dermatitis venenata from English ivy (*Hedera helix*). Arch. Dermatol. 74:311–312.

Goldsmith, W.W. 1909. Onion poisoning in cattle. Comp. Path. Ther. 22:151.

Gooneratne, B.W.M. 1966. Massive generalized alopecia after poisoning by *Gloriosa superba*. Br. Med. J. 1:1023–1024.

Graham, R.; Boughton, I.B. 1925. White snakeroot poisoning. Ill. Agric. Exp. Stn. Circ. 295. 7 pp.

Greatorex, J.C. 1966. Some unusual cases of plant poisoning in animals. Vet. Rec. 78:725–727.

Gress, E.M. 1935. Poisonous plants of Pennsylvania. Penn. Dep. Agric. Gen. Bull. 531. 51 pp.

Groh, H. 1941. The distribution of bracken and its possible relations to bovine hematuria in British Columbia. Sci. Agric. 21:703–710.

Guin, J.D. 1980. Reaction time in experimental poison ivy dermatitis. Contact Dermatitis 6:289–290.

Gunby, P. 1980. Keep away from that "tree" folks. J. Am. Med. Assoc. 244:2596.

Gunn, C.R. 1969. *Abrus precatorius*: A deadly gift. N.Y. Bot. Gard. J. 19:2–5.

Güssow, H.T. 1912. Horsetail, *Equisetum arvense* L. Can. Dep. Agric. Exp. Farms Rep. 1912:210.

Gwatkin, R.; Moynihan, I.W. 1943. Wild mustard seed poisoning in cattle. Can. J. Comp. Med. 7:76–77.

Hadwen, S. 1917. So-called staggers in horses caused by the ingestion of *Pteris aquilina*, the common bracken. J. Am. Vet. Med. Assoc. n.s. 3:701–704.

Hadwen, S.; Bruce, E.A. 1933. The poisoning of horses by the common bracken (*Pteris aquilina* L.). Vet. J. 89:120–128.

Haggerty, D.R.; Conway, J.A. 1936. Report of poisoning by *Cicuta maculata*. N.Y. State J. Med. 36:1511–1514.

Halstead, B.A. 1899. The poisonous plants of New Jersey. N.J. Agric. Exp. Stn. Bull. 135. 28 pp.

Hannam, D.A.R. 1985. Hemlock (*Conium maculatum*) poisoning in the pig. Vet. Rec. 116:322.

Hansen, A.A. 1924a. A unique field experiment with white snake-root. J. Am. Vet. Med. Assoc. 65:224–226.

Hansen, A.A. 1924b. The poison plant situation in Indiana. III. J. Am. Vet. Med. Assoc. 65:351–362.

Hansen, A.A. 1924c. Robitin—A potent plant poison. Better Crops 2:22–23, 44.

Hansen, A.A. 1925a. The poisonous plant situation in Indiana. II. J. Am. Vet. Med. Assoc. 66:80–92.

Hansen, A.A. 1925b. Two fatal cases of potato poisoning. Science 61:340–341.

Hansen, A.A. 1927. Stock poisoning by plants in the nightshade family. J. Am. Vet. Med. Assoc. 71:221–227.

Hansen, A.A. 1928a. The tragedy of Hindostan. Nat. Mag. 11:385–386.

Hansen, A.A. 1928b. The latest developments in the stock-poisoning plant situation in Indiana. J. Am. Vet. Med. Assoc. 73:471–474.

Hansen, A.A. 1928c. Stock poisoning plants. N. Am. Vet. 9:32–36.

Hansen, A.A. 1928d. Stock poisoning plants. Cocklebur. N. Am. Vet. 9:46–49.

Hansen, A.A. 1928e. Trifoliosis and similar stock diseases. N. Am. Vet. 9:34–36.

Hansen, A.A. 1928f. Potato poisoning. N. Am. Vet. 9:31–34.

Hansen, A.A. 1928g. *Cicuta* or water hemlock poisoning. N. Am. Vet. 9:34–39.

Hansen, A.A. 1930. Indiana plants injurious to livestock. Purdue Univ. Agric. Exp. Stn. Circ. 175. 38 pp.

Hardin, J.W.; Arena, J.M. 1974. Human poisoning from native and cultivated plants. 2nd ed. Duke Univ. Press, Durham, N.C. 194 pp.

Harlow, W.M. 1946. Poison ivy and poison sumac. N.Y. State Coll. For. Bull. 19. 19 pp.

Harshberger, J.W. 1920. Pastoral and agricultural botany. Blakistons Son & Co., Philadelphia, Pa. 294 pp.

Hausen, B.M.; Brohan, J.; Koenig, W.A.; Faasch, H.; Hahn, H.; Bruhn, G. 1987. Allergic and irritant contact dermatitis from falcarinol and didehydrofalcarinol in common ivy, *Hedera helix* L. Contact Dermatitis 17:1–9.

Henderson, J.A.M.; DesGroseilliers, J.P. 1984. Gas plant (*Dictamnus albus*) phytophotodermatitis simulating poison ivy. Can. Med. Assoc. J. 130:889–891.

Hershey, A.L. 1945. Some poisonous plant problems of New Mexico. State Coll. New Mexico. Agric. Exp. Stn. Bull. 322. 23 pp.

Heuser, G.F.; Schumacher, A.E. 1942. The feeding of corn cockle to chickens. Poult. Sci. 21:86–93.

Heyl, F.W.; Loy, S.K.; Knight, H.G.; Prien, O.L. 1912. The chemical examination of death camas. Univ. Wyo. Agric. Exp. Stn. Bull. 94. 31 pp.

Hocking, G.M. 1947. Henbane—Healing herbs of Hercules and of Apollo. Econ. Bot. 1:306–316.

Hodgdon, A.R. 1951. Is *Onoclea sensibilis* poisonous to horses? Am. Fern J. 41:61–62.

Hogg, A.; Hibbs, C.M. 1976. Nitrate poisoning in cattle. Vet. Toxicol. 18:41.

Hoy, D.L.; Catling, P.M. 1981. Necklaces from nature-seed jewelery. Davidsonia 12:63–77.

Hubbs, J.C. 1947. Belladonna poisoning in pigs. Vet. Med. 42:428–429.

Hughes, J.D.; Clark, J.A. 1939. Stramonium poisoning. J. Am. Med. Assoc. 112:2500–2503.

Hutchison, T.W.S. 1977. Onions as a cause of heinz body anaemia and death in cattle. Can. Vet. J. 18:358–360.

Huxtable, R.J. 1980. Herbal teas and toxins: Novel aspects of pyrrolizidine poisoning in the United States. Perspect. Biol. Med. 24:1–14.

Hymans, C.W. 1898. Medicinal plants. N.C. Agric. Exp. Stn. Bull. 150:331–409.

Ivie, G.W.; Witzel, D.A. 1983. Sesquiterpene lactones: Structure, biological action, and toxicological significance. Pages 543–584 in Keeler, R.F.; Tu, A.T., eds. Handbook of natural toxins. Vol. 1. Plant and fungal toxins. Marcel Dekker Inc., New York, N.Y.

Jacobziner, H.; Raybin, H.W. 1960. Internal drug poisoning including three fatalities. N.Y. State J. Med. 60:3139–3142.

Jacobziner, H.; Raybin, H.W. 1961a. Plant and insecticide poisonings. N.Y. State J. Med. 61:2463.

Jacobziner, H.; Raybin, H.W. 1961b. Fatal salicylate intoxication and stramonium poisoning. N.Y. State J. Med. 61:301–303.

Jaeckle, K.A.; Freemon, F.R. 1981. Pokeweed poisoning. South. Med. J. 74:639–640.

James, L.F.; Bennett, K.L.; Parker, K.G.; Keeler, R.F.; Binns, W.; Lindsay, B. 1968. Locoweed poisoning in sheep. J. Range Manage. 21:360–365.

James, L.F.; Hartley, W.J.; Nielsen, D.; Allen, S.; Panter, K.E. 1986. Locoweed (Oxytropis sericea) poisoning and congestive heart failure in cattle. J. Am. Vet. Med. Assoc. 189:1549–1556.

James, L.F.; Hartley, W.J.; Van Kampen, K.R. 1981. Syndromes of Astragalus poisoning in livestock. J. Am. Vet. Med. Assoc. 178:146–150.

James, L.F.; Nielsen, D.B. 1988. Locoweeds: Assessment of the problem on western U.S. rangelands. Pages 171–180 in James, L.F., et al., eds. The ecology and economic impact of poisonous plants on livestock production. Westview Press, Boulder, Colo.

James, L.F.; Ralphs, M.H.; Nielsen, D.B. (eds.). 1988. The ecology and economic impact of poisonous plants on livestock production. Westview Press, Boulder, Colo. 428 pp.

James, L.F.; Williams, M.C.; Bleak, A.T. 1976. Toxicity of Bassia hyssopifolia to sheep. J. Range Manage. 29:284–285.

Jennings, R.E. 1935. Stramonium poisoning. J. Pediatr. 6:657–664.

Jessup, D.A.; Boermans, H.J.; Kock, N.D. 1986. Toxicosis in the tule elk caused by ingestion of poison hemlock. J. Am. Vet. Med. Assoc. 189:1173–1175.

Johnston, A.; Peake, R.W. 1960. Effect of selective grazing on sheep on the control of leafy spurge (Euphorbia esula L.). J. Range Manage. 12:192.

Johnston, A.; Smoliak, S.; Avery, R.J. 1965. Veterinarian's handbook of poisonous and injurious plants of the Prairie Provinces. Agric. Can. Res. Stn., Lethbridge, Alta. 54 pp.

Johnston, A; Smoliak, S.; Wroe, R.A. 1975. Poisonous and injurious plants of Alberta. Alberta Agric. Agdex 666-1. 60 pp.

Jordan, E.O.; Harris, N.M. 1909. Milksickness. J. Infect. Dis. 6:401–491.

Kalkus, J.W.; Tripeer, H.A.; Fuller, J.R. 1925. Enzootic hepatic cirrhosis of horses (walking disease) in the Pacific northwest. J. Am. Vet. Med. Assoc. 68:285–298.

Kaufmann, G.W. 1982. Seasonal variation of tremetol concentrations found in white snakeroot, *Eupatorium rugosum* Houtt. (Compositae). Proc. Iowa Acad. Sci. 89:151–152.

Kaymakcalan, S. 1964. Fatal poisoning with *Podophyllum* resin. J. Am. Med. Assoc. 190:558.

Keeler, R.F. 1973. Lupin alkaloids from teratogenic and non-teratogenic lupins II. Identification of the major alkaloids by tandem gas chromatography–mass spectrometry in plants producing crooked calf disease. Teratology 7:31–36.

Keeler, R.F. 1974. Coniine, a teratogenic principle from *Conium maculatum* producing malformation in calves. Clin. Toxicol. 7:195–206.

Keeler, R.F. 1983. Deformed calves from poisonous plants. Rangelands 5:221–223.

Keeler, R.F. 1988. Livestock models of human birth defects, reviewed in relation to poisonous plants. J. Anim. Sci. 66:2414–2427.

Keeler, R.F.; James, L.F.; Shupe, J.L.; Van Kampen, K.R. 1977. Lupine-induced crooked calf disease and a management method to reduce incidence. J. Range Manage. 30:97–102.

Keeler, R.F.; Johnson, A.E.; Chase, R.L. 1986. Toxicity of *Thermopsis montana* in cattle. Cornell Vet. 76:115–127.

Keeler, R.F.; Tu, A.T. (eds.). 1983. Handbook of natural toxins. Vol. 1. Plant and fungal toxins. Marcel Dekker Inc., New York, N.Y. 934 pp.

Keeler, R.F.; Van Kampen, K.R.; James, L.F. (eds.). 1978. Effects of poisonous plants on livestock. Academic Press, New York, N.Y. 600 pp.

Kelleway, R.A.; Geovjian, L. 1978. Acute bracken fern poisoning in a 14-month-old horse. Vet. Med. Small Anim. Clin. 73:295–296.

Kennedy, P.C. 1957. Case 16—Tarweed poisoning in swine. J. Am. Vet. Med. Assoc. 130:305–306.

Kerr, L.A.; Edwards, W.C. 1982. Hairy vetch poisoning in cattle. Vet. Med. 77:257–258.

King, E.D., Jr. 1923. Jimsonweed poisoning. J. Am. Vet. Med. Assoc. 64:98–99.

Kinghorn, A.D. 1977. Toxic plants. Columbia Univ. Press, New York. 195 pp.

Kingsbury, J.M. 1961. Knowledge of poisonous plants in the United States—Brief history and conclusions. Econ. Bot. 15:119–130.

Kingsbury, J.M. 1964. Poisonous plants of the United States and Canada. Prentice-Hall, Englewood Cliffs, N.J. 626 pp.

Kligman, A.M. 1958. Poison ivy (*Rhus*) dermatitis. Am. Med. Assoc. Arch. Dermatol. 77:149–180.

Klingman, D.L. 1963. Poison ivy and poison oak. U.S. Dep. Agric. Farmer's Bull. 1972. 22 pp.

Knight, A.P. 1987. Rhododendron and laurel poisonings. Compend. Food Anim. 9:F26–F27.

Knight, A.P.; Kimberling, C.V.; Stermitz, F.R.; Roby, M.R. 1984. *Cynoglossum officinale* (hound's-tongue)—A case of pyrrolizidine alkaloid poisoning in horses. J. Am. Vet. Med. Assoc. 185:647–650.

Koch, R.B.; Leon, L.C. 1981. Effects of urushiol compounds isolated from poison ivy ATPase activities. Biochem. Pharmacol. 30:1133–1135.

Koopman, H. 1937. A fatal case of celandine poisoning. Sammlung von Vergiftungsfällen 8:93–98.

Kozlov, V.A.; Gulyaeva, T.N. 1983. Poisoning by the fruit of the common privet. Sud. Med. Ekspert. 26:56–57.

Krause, G.L.; Weidman, F.D. 1925. Ivy poisoning. J. Am. Med. Assoc. 84:1996–1999.

Kürkçüoglu, M. 1970. Henbane (*Hyoscyamus niger*) poisonings in the vicinity of Erzurum. Turk. J. Pediatr. 12:48–56.

Lacey, J.R.; James, L.F.; Short, R.E. 1988. Ponderosa pine: Economic impact. Pages 95–106 in James, L.F., et al., eds. The ecology and economic impact of poisonous plants on livestock production. Westview Press, Boulder, Colo.

Lamoureux, G. et collaborateurs. 1975. Les plantes sauvages printanières. Éditeur officiel du Québec, Québec. 247 pp.

Lampe, K. 1978. Systematic plant poisoning in children. Pediatrics 54:347–351.

Lampe, K.F.; McCann, M.A. 1985. AMA handbook of poisonous and injurious plants. Chicago Review Press, Chicago, Ill. 432 pp.

Langham, R.F. 1957. Case 20—Bracken fern poisoning in a cow. J. Am. Vet. Med. Assoc. 130:334–335.

Leach, D.G. 1966. History of rhododendron poisoning. Garden J. 16:215–217, 237.

Leach, D.G. 1967. The history of rhododendron poisoning. Garden J. 17:15–18, 33.

Leipold, H.W.; Oehme, F.W.; Cook, J.E. 1973. Congenital arthrogryposis associated with ingestion of jimsonweed by pregnant sows. J. Am. Vet. Med. Assoc. 162:1059–1060.

Lessard, P; Wilson, W.D.; Olander, H.J.; Rogers, Q.R.; Mendel, V.E. 1986. Clinicopathologic study of horses surviving pyrrolizidine alkaloid (Senecio vulgaris) toxicosis. Am. J. Vet. Res. 47:1776–1780.

Levy, R. 1976. Jimson weed poisoning. Ann. Stern. Med. 84:223.

Lewis, W.H. 1979. Snowberry (Symphoricarpus) poisoning in children. J. Am. Med. Assoc. 242:2663.

Lewis, W.H.; Elvin-Lewis, M.P.F. 1977. Medical botany; plants affecting man's health. Wiley, New York, N.Y. 515 pp.

Lewis, W.H.; Smith, P.R. 1979. Poke root herbal tea poisoning. J. Am. Med. Assoc. 242:2759–2760.

Litovitz, T.L.; Fahey, B.A. 1982. Please don't eat the daffodils. N. Engl. J. Med. 306:547.

Lodge, R.W.; McLean, A.; Johnston, A. 1968. Stock-poisoning plants of western Canada. Agric. Can. Publ. 1361. 34 pp.

Loev, B.; Dawson, C.R. 1956. On the geometrical configuration of the olefinic components of poison ivy urushiol. The synthesis of a model compound. J. Am. Chem. Soc. 78:1180–1183.

Long, H.C. 1917. Plants poisonous to livestock. Cambridge Univ. Press, Cambridge, Mass. 119 pp.

Long, H.C. 1934. Poisonous plants on the farm. Minist. Agric. Fish. London Bull. 75. 52 pp.

Looman, J.; Majak, W.; Smoliak, S. 1983. Stock-poisoning plants of Western Canada. Agric. Can. Res. Br. Contrib. 1982-7E. 36 pp.

Lorenz, R.J.; Dewey, S.A. 1988. Noxious weeds that are poisonous. Pages 309–323 in James, L.F., et al., eds. The ecology and economic impact of poisonous plants on livestock production. Westview Press, Boulder, Colo.

Löve, D.; Dansereau, P. 1959. Biosystematic studies on Xanthium: Taxonomic appraisal and ecological status. Can. J. Bot. 37:173–208.

Lowe, J.E.; Hintz, H.F.; Schryver, H.F.; Kingsbury, J.M. 1970. Taxus cuspidata (Japanese yew) poisoning in horses. Cornell Vet. 60:36–39.

Macaulay, J.C. 1987. Orchid allergy. Contact Dermatitis 17:112–113.

MacDonald, M.A. 1952a. Timber milk vetch poisoning on British Columbia ranges. J. Range Manage. 52:16.

MacDonald, M.A. 1952b. Pine needle abortion in range beef cattle. J. Range Manage. 5:150–155.

Malizia, E.; Sarcinelli, L; Andreucei, G. 1977. *Ricinus* poisoning: A familiar epidemy. Acta Pharmacol. Toxicol. Suppl. 41:351–361.

Marie-Victorin, F. 1964. Flore Laurentienne (deuxième édition). Univ. Montréal, Montréal, Qué. 925 pp.

Marsh, C.D. 1909. The loco-weed disease of the plains. U.S. Dep. Agric. Bull. 112. 129 pp.

Marsh, C.D. 1914. *Menziesia*, a new stock-poisoning plant of the northwestern States. U.S. Dep. Agric. Bur. Plant Ind., Gen. Publ. 16. 3 pp.

Marsh, C.D. 1919. The locoweed disease. U.S. Dep. Agric. Farmers' Bull. 1054. 19 pp.

Marsh, C.D. 1929a. Stock-poisoning plants of the range. Revised. U.S. Dep. Agric. Bull. 1245. 74 pp.

Marsh, C.D. 1929b. Trembles. U.S. Dep. Agric. Farmers' Bull. 1593. 10 pp.

Marsh, C.D.; Clawson, A.B. 1921. Poisonous properties of the whorled milkweeds *Asclepias pumila* and *A. verticillata* var. *geyeri*. U.S. Dep. Agric. Bull. 942. 14 pp.

Marsh, C.D.; Clawson, A.B. 1922. The death camas species, *Zygadenus paniculatus* and *Z. elegans*, as poisonous plants. U.S. Dep. Agric. Bull. 1012. 25 pp.

Marsh, C.D.; Clawson, A.B. 1924. The meadow death camas (*Zygadenus venenosus*) as a poisonous plant. U.S. Dep. Agric. Bull. 1240. 13 pp.

Marsh, C.D.; Clawson, A.B. 1930a. Mountain laurel (*Kalmia latifolia*) and sheep laurel (*Kalmia angustifolia*) as stock-poisoning plants. U.S. Dep. Agric. Tech. Bull. 219. 22 pp.

Marsh, C.D.; Clawson, A.B. 1930b. Toxic effects of St. John's-wort (*Hypericum perforatum*) on cattle and sheep. U.S. Dep. Agric. Tech. Bull. 202. 23 pp.

Marsh, C.D.; Clawson, A.B.; Marsh, H. 1915. *Zygadenus*, or death camas. U.S. Dep. Agric. Bull. 125. 46 pp.

Marsh, C.D.; Clawson, A.B.; Marsh, H. 1916. Lupines as poisonous plants. U.S. Dep. Agric. Bull. 405. 45 pp.

Marsh, C.D.; Clawson, A.B.; Marsh, H. 1923a. Larkspur or "poison-weed." U.S. Agric. Farmers' Bull. 988. 15 pp.

Marsh, C.D.; Clawson, A.B.; Roe, G.C. 1929. Arrow grass (*Triglochin maritima*) as a stock-poisoning plant. U.S. Dep. Agric. Tech. Bull. 113. 15 pp.

Marsh, C.D.; Roe, G.C.; Clawson, A.B. 1923b. Livestock poisoning by cocklebur. U.S. Dep. Agric. Circ. 283. 4 pp.

Marsh, C.D.; Roe, G.C.; Clawson, A.B. 1924. Cockelburs (species of *Xanthium*) as poisonous plants. U.S. Dep. Agric. Bull. 1274. 24 pp.

Martin, T.; Morgan, S. 1987. What caused the photosensitivity in these dairy heifers? Vet. Med. 82:848–851.

Martin, T.; Stair, E.L.; Dawson, L. 1986. Cocklebur poisoning in cattle. J. Am. Vet. Med. Assoc. 189:562–563.

Massmanian, A.; Cavero, F.V.; Bosca, A.R.; Rodellas, A.C. 1988. Contact dermatitis from variegated ivy (*Hedera helix* subsp. *canariensis* Willd.). Contact Dermatitis 18:247–248.

McCulloch, E.C. 1940. Hepatic cirrhosis of horses, swine and cattle due to the ingestion of seeds of tarweed, *Amsinckia intermedia*. J. Am. Vet. Med. Assoc. 96:5–18.

McDaniel, K.C.; Loomis, L.E. 1985. Livestock poisoning by perennial snakeweeds. Weeds Today 16:9–11.

McDaniel, K.C.; Sosebee, R.E. 1988. Ecology, management and poisonous properties associated with perennial snakeweeds. Pages 43–56 *in* James, L.F., et al., eds. The ecology and economic impact of poisonous plants on livestock production. Westview Press, Boulder, Colo.

McGee, M.D. 1973. Rhododendron ingestion. Natl. Clgh. Poison Control Cent. Bull., Sept./Oct.:1–2.

McIntosh, K.L. 1980. Harmful plants. Fac. Med., Univ. Toronto, Toronto, Ont. 61 pp.

McIntosh, R.A. 1928. May apple poisoning in a cow. Ont. Vet. Coll. Rep. 29:18–20.

McLean, A.; Nicholson, H.H. 1958. Stock-poisoning plants of the British Columbia ranges. Agric. Can. Publ. 1037. 30 pp.

McMillan, M.; Thompson, J.C. 1979. An outbreak of suspected solanine poisoning in school boys. J. Med. (New Series) 48:227–243.

McNair, J.B. 1921. The transmission of *Rhus* poison from plant to person. Am. J. Bot. 8:238–250.

McNair, J.B. 1923. *Rhus* dermatitis from *Rhus toxicodendron, radicans* and *diversiloba*. Univ. Chicago Press, Chicago, Ill. 298 pp.

Menges, R.W.; Selby, L.A.; Marienfeld, C.J.; Aue, W.A.; Greer, D.L. 1970. A tobacco related epidemic of congenital limb deformities in swine. Environ. Res. 3:285.

Mettler, F.A.; Stern, G.M. 1963. Observations on the toxic effects of yellow star thistle. J. Neuropathol. Exp. Neurol. 22:164–169.

Mikolich, J.R. 1975. Acute anticholinergic syndrome due to jimson weed ingestion. Ann. Intern. Med. 83:321–325.

Millspaugh, C.F. 1887. American medicinal plants. Vol. I. Boericke and Tafel, New York, 109 sections.

Milne, R. 1988. Heathlands of England harbour cancer spores. New Sci. 1608:23.

Mitchell, J.; Rook, A. 1979. Botanical dermatology—plants and plant products injurious to the skin. Greengrass, Vancouver, B.C. 787 pp.

Mitchell, J.E.; Mitchell, F.N. 1955. Jimson weed (*Datura stramonium*) poisoning in childhood. J. Pediatr. 47:227–230.

Montgomery, F.H.; Henderson, J.A.; Bibbey, R.O. 1955. Plants poisonous to livestock in Ontario. Ont. Dep. Agric. Bull. 508. 39 pp.

Moore, D.W. 1976. The autumnal high: Jimsonweed in North Carolina. N.C. Med. J. 37:492–495.

Morse, F.W.; Howard, C.D. 1898. Poisonous properties of wild cherry leaves. N.H. Coll. Agric. Exp. Stn. Bull. 56:113–123.

Morton, J.F. 1958. Ornamental plants with poisonous properties. Proc. Fla. State Hortic. Soc. 71:372–380.

Morton, J.F. 1962. Ornamental plants with toxic and/or irritant properties. 2. Proc. Fla. State Hortic. Soc. 75:484–491.

Morton, J.K. 1975. The giant cow parsnip, *Heracleum mantegazzianum*, Umbelliferae, in Canada. Can. Field-Nat. 89:183–184.

Moseley, E.L. 1906. The cause of trembles in cattle, sheep and horses, and of milksickness in people. Ohio Nat. 6:463–483.

Moseley, E.L. 1941. Milksickness caused by white snakeroot. Ohio Acad. Sci., Bowling Green, Ohio. 171 pp.

Muenscher, W.C. 1948. Leafy spurge and related weeds. Revised. N.Y. State Coll. Agric. Ext. Bull. 192. 12 pp.

Muenscher, W.C. 1951. Poisonous plants of the United States. 2nd ed. Macmillan, New York, N.Y. 266 pp.

Muenscher, W.C. 1975. Poisonous plants of the United States. Revised Ed. Collier Books, New York, N.Y. 277 pp.

Mulligan, G.A. 1980a. Poison-ivy, western poison oak and poison sumac. Agric. Can. Publ. 1699. 13 pp.

Mulligan, G.A. 1980b. The genus *Cicuta* in North America. Can. J. Bot. 58:1755–1767.

Mulligan, G.A. 1987. Common weeds of Canada. Revised. NC Press Ltd., Toronto, Ont. 143 pp.

Mulligan, G.A.; Bailey, L.G. 1975. The biology of Canadian weeds. 8. *Sinapis arvensis* L. Can. J. Plant Sci. 55:171–183.

Mulligan, G.A.; Junkins, B.E. 1977. The biology of Canadian weeds. 23. *Rhus radicans* L. Can. J. Plant Sci. 57:515–523.

Mulligan, G.A.; Munro, D.B. 1981*a*. The biology of Canadian weeds. 51. *Prunus virginiana* L. and *P. serotina* Ehrh. Can. J. Plant Sci. 61:977–992.

Mulligan, G.A.; Munro, D.B. 1981*b*. The biology of Canadian weeds. 48. *Cicuta maculata* L., *C. douglasii* (DC.) Coult. & Rose and *C. virosa* L. Can. J. Plant Sci. 61:93–105.

Mulligan, G.A.; Munro, D.B. 1983. Vascular plants poisonous to livestock in Canada: 1. A preliminary inventory. Agric. Can. Res. Br. Contrib. 1983–23E. 33 pp.

Mulligan, G.A.; Munro, D.B. 1984. Wild and cultivated plants poisonous to humans in Canada: A preliminary inventory. Agric. Can. Res. Br. Tech. Bull. 1984–15E. 22 pp.

Mulligan, G.A.; Munro, D.B. 1987. The biology of Canadian weeds. 77. *Veratrum viride* Ait. Can. J. Plant Sci. 67:777–786.

Munz, P.A. 1965. Dermatitis produced by *Phacelia*. Science 76:194.

Nakamura, T. 1985. Ginko tree (*Ginkgo biloba*) dermatitis. Contact Dermatitis 12:281–282.

Nation, P.N.; Benn, M.H.; Roth, S.H.; Wilkens, J.L. 1982. Clinical signs and studies of the site of action of purified larkspur alkaloid, methyllycaconitine, administered parenterally to calves. Can. Vet. J. 23:264–266.

Nielsen, D.B.; Ralphs, M.H. 1988. Larkspur: Economic consideration. Pages 119–129 *in* James, L.F., et al., eds. The ecology and economic impact of poisonous plants on livestock production. Westview Press, Boulder, Colo.

Niyogi, S.K. 1970. The toxicology of *Abrus precatorius* L. J. Forensic Sci. 15:529–536.

Ogden, P.R.; Welsh, S.L.; Williams, M.C.; Ralphs, M.H. 1988. *Astragalus* and related genera—ecological considerations. Pages 153–169 *in* James, L.F., et al., eds. The ecology and economic impact of poisonous plants on livestock production. Westview Press, Boulder, Colo.

Ogg, A.G., Jr.; Rogers, B.S.; Schilling, E.E. 1981. Characterization of black nightshade (*Solanum nigrum*) and related species in the United States. Weed Sci. 29:27–32.

O'Leary, S.B.; Hyattsville, W. 1964. Poisoning in man from eating poisonous plants. Environ. Health (Lond.) 9:216–242.

Olson, C.T.; Keller, W.C.; Gerken, D.F.; Reed, S.M. 1984. Suspected tremetol poisoning in horses. J. Am. Vet. Med. Assoc. 185:1001–1003.

Osweiler, G.D.; Buck, W.B.; Bicknell, E.J. 1969. Production of perirenal edema in swine with *Amaranthus retroflexus*. Am. J. Vet. Res. 30:557–566.

Pammel, L.H. 1917*a*. Young sneezeweed poisonous. Am. J. Vet. Med. 12:461–462.

Pammel, L.H. 1917*b*. Poisoning from oaks. Am. J. Vet. Med. 12:323–324, 339.

Pammel, L.H. 1919. Poison hemlock. Am. J. Vet. Med. 14:513–514.

Pammel, L.H. 1921. Western poison cowbane. Am. J. Vet. Med. 16:33.

Pammel, L.H. 1928. Golden glow is injurious. Vet. Med. 23:28.

Pamucku, A.M.; Yalciner, S.; Bryan, G.T. 1977. Inhibition of carcinogenic effect of bracken fern (*Pteridium aquilinum*) by various chemicals. Cancer Suppl. 40:2450–2454.

Panciera, R.J. 1978. Hairy vetch (*Vicia villosa* Roth) poisoning in cattle. Pages 555–563 *in* Keeler, R.F., et al., eds. Effects of poisonous plants on livestock. Academic Press, New York, N.Y.

Panter, K.E.; Bunch, T.D.; Keeler, R.F. 1988*a*. Maternal and fetal toxicity of poison hemlock (*Conium maculatum*) in sheep. Am. J. Vet. Res. 49:281–283.

Panter, K.E.; James, L.F.; Baker, D.C.; Short, R.E. 1987. Pine needle toxicoses in cattle and goats. Anim. Sci. 65:351–352.

Panter, K.E.; James, L.F.; Molyneux, R.J.; Baker, D.C.; Short, R.E. 1988*b*. Effects of various parts of the ponderosa pine on bovine pregnancy. Am. Soc. Anim. Sci. 66:372.

Panter, K.E.; Keeler, R.F. 1988. The hemlocks: Poison-hemlock (*Conium maculatum*) and water-hemlock (*Cicuta* spp.). Pages 207–225 *in* James, L.F., et al., eds. The ecology and economic impact of poisonous plants on livestock production. Westview Press, Boulder, Colo.

Panter, K.E.; Keeler, R.F.; Baker, D.C. 1988*c*. Toxicoses in livestock from the hemlocks (*Conium* and *Cicuta* spp.). J. Anim. Sci. 66:2407–2413.

Panter, K.E.; Keeler, R.F.; Buck, W.B. 1985. Congenital skeletal malformations induced by maternal ingestion of *Conium maculatum* (poison hemlock) in newborn pigs. Am. J. Vet. Res. 46:2064–2066.

Panter, K.E.; Ralphs, M.H. 1987. Death camas poisoning in sheep: A case report. Vet. Hum. Toxicol. 29:45–47.

Pardee, K. 1847. Case of poisoning by wild cherry. West. Lancet 6:289–291.

Parker, K.W. 1936. Prevention of death losses in sheep in areas infested with pingue (*Actinea richardsonii*). N.M. Agric. Exp. Stn. Bull. 241. 53 pp.

Patterson, F.D. 1929. Pokeweed causes heavy losses in swine herd. Vet. Med. 24:114.

Pethick, W.H. 1921. Pictou cattle disease, with special reference to the symptomatology. Can. Vet. Rec. 2:13–16.

Phares, D.L. 1889. Diseases of sheep and calves. Miss. Agric. Exp. Stn. Bull. 9:11–13.

Pijoan, M. 1942. Cyanide poisoning from choke cherry seed. Am. J. Med. Sci. 204:550–553.

Pohl, R.W. 1961. Poisoning by *Dieffenbachia*. J. Am. Med. Assoc. 177:812.

Polk, I.J. 1981. Poison ivy and oak make (almost) everyone itch. J. Am. Med. Assoc. 246:784.

Pritchard, W.R. 1956. Laurel (*Kalmia angustifolia*) poisoning of sheep. N. Am. Vet. 37:461–462.

Puls, R.; Newschwander, F.P.; Greenway, J.A. 1978. Cyanide poisoning from *Glyceria grandis* (tall mannagrass) in British Columbia. Can. Vet. J. 19:264–265.

Quigley, G.D.; Waite, R.H. 1931. Miscellaneous feeding trials with poultry. I. The effects of corn cockle on poultry. Univ. Md. Agric. Exp. Stn. Bull. 325:343–354.

Ralphs, M.H.; Sharp, L.A. 1988. Management to reduce losses from poisonous plants. Pages 391–405 *in* James, L.F., et al., eds. The ecology and economic impact of poisonous plants on livestock production. Westview Press, Boulder, Colo.

Reddock, A.H.; Reddock, J.M. 1984. Warning: Lady's-slipper can be hazardous to your health. Plant Press Field Bot. Ont. Newsl. 2:10.

Reynard, G.B.; Norton, J.B.S. 1942. Poisonous plants of Maryland in relation to livestock. Univ. Md. Agric. Exp. Stn. Tech. Bull. A10:249–312.

Rich, F.A.; Jones, L.R. 1902. A poisonous plant, the common horsetail. Vt. Agric. Exp. Stn. Bull. 95:187–192.

Robb, H.F. 1919. Death from rhubarb leaves due to oxalic acid poisoning. J. Am. Med. Assoc. 73:627–628.

Robson, P. 1965. Water hemlock poisoning. Lancet 288:1274–1275.

Rodrigues, T.D.; Johnson, P.N.; Jeffrey, L.P. 1984. Holly berry ingestion: A case report. Vet. Hum. Toxicol. 26:157–158.

Rosenberger, G. 1971. Nature, manifestations, cause and control of chronic enzootic haemeturia in cattle. Vet. Med. Rev. 2/3:189–206.

Sampson, A.W.; Malmsten, H.E. 1935. Stock-poisoning plants of California. Univ. Calif. Agric. Exp. Stn. Bull. 593. 89 pp.

Sampson, A.W.; Parker, K.W. 1930. St. Johnswort on range lands in California. Calif. Agric. Exp. Stn. Bull. 503. 48 pp.

Sandusky, G.E.; Fosnaugh, C.J.; Smith, J.B.; Mohan, R. 1977. Oak poisoning of cattle in Ohio. J. Am. Vet. Med. Assoc. 171:627–629.

Sauer, J.D. 1950. Pokeweed, an old American herb. Mo. Bot. Gard. Bull. 5:82–88.

Schaffner, J.H. 1903. Poisonous and other injurious plants of Ohio. Ohio Nat. 4:16–19, 32–35, 69–73.

Schulte, T. 1975. Fatal poisoning from yew needles (*Taxus baccata*). Arch. Toxicol. 34:153–158.

Schuster, J.L.; James, L.F. 1988. Some other major poisonous plants of the western United States. Pages 295–307 *in* James, L.F., et al., eds. The ecology and economic impact of poisonous plants on livestock production. Westview Press, Boulder, Colo.

Schwartz, R.S.; Downham, T.F. 1981. Erythema multiforme associated with *Rhus* contact dermatitis. Cutis 27:85–86.

Seiber, J.N.; Lee, S.M.; Benson, J.M. 1983. Cardiac glycosides (Cardenolides) in species of *Asclepias*. Pages 43–83 *in* Keeler, R.F.; Tu, A.T., eds. Handbook of natural toxins. Vol. 1. Plant and fungal toxins. Marcel Dekker Inc., New York, N.Y.

Selye, H. 1957. Lathyrism. Rev. Can. Biol. 16:1–82.

Sharrow, S.H.; Ueckert, D.N.; Johnson, A.E. 1988. Ecology and toxicology of *Senecio* species with special reference to *Senecio jacobaea* and *Senecio longilobus*. Pages 181–196 *in* James, L.F., et al., eds. The ecology and economic impact of poisonous plants on livestock production. Westview Press, Boulder, Colo.

Shaw, D.; Pearn, J. 1979. Oleander poisoning. Med. J. Aust. 2:267–269.

Shaw, R.J.; Williams, M.C. 1986. Consider the lilies of the field. Utah Sci. 47:30–35.

Shelmire, B. 1941. The poison ivy plant and its oleoresin. J. Invest. Dermatol. 4:337–348.

Shupe, J.L.; Binns, W.; James, L.F.; Keeler, R.F. 1967. Lupine, a cause of crooked calf disease. J. Am. Vet. Med. Assoc. 151:198–203.

Skidmore, L.V. 1933. Water hemlock (*Cicuta maculata* L.) poisoning in swine. Vet. J. 89:76–80.

Skidmore, L.V.; Peterson, N.F. 1932. Observations on the toxicity of golden glow (*Rudbeckia laciniata*) to swine and other animals. J. Am. Vet. Med. Assoc. 81:655–662.

Smith, R.A. 1987. Potential edible lupine poisonings in humans. Vet. Hum. Toxicol. 29:444–445.

Smith, R.A.; Crowe, S.P. 1987. Fanweed toxicosis in cattle: Case history, analytical method, suggested treatment, and fanweed detoxification. Vet. Hum. Toxicol. 29:155–156.

Spoerke, D.D.; Spoerke, S.E. 1979. Three cases of *Zigadenus* (death camas) poisoning. Vet. Hum. Toxicol. 21:346–347.

Spoerke, D.G.; Hall, A.H.; Dodson, C.D.; Stermitz, F.R.; Swanson, C.H.; Rumack, B.H. 1987. Mystery root ingestion. Emerg. Med. 5:385–388.

Stahevitch, A.E.; Crompton, C.W.; Wojtas, W.A. 1988. The biology of Canadian weeds. 85. *Euphorbia cyparissias* L. Can. J. Plant Sci. 68:175–191.

Staley, E. 1976. A treatment for tansy mustard poisoning. Bovine Pract. 11:35.

Starreveld, E.; Hope, C.E. 1975. Cicutoxin poisoning (water-hemlock). Neurology 25:730–734.

Steyn, D.G. 1934. The toxicology of plants in South Africa. Central News Agency, South Africa. 631 pp.

Stiles, F.C. 1951. Stramonium poisoning. J. Pediatr. 39:354–356.

Stockman, R. 1929. Lathyrism. Pharmacol. Exp. Ther. 37:43–53.

Stuart, B.P.; Nicholson, S.S.; Smith, J.B. 1975. Perirenal edema and toxic nephrosis in cattle associated with ingestion of pigweed. J. Am. Vet. Med. Assoc. 187:949.

Symes, W.F.; Dawson, C.R. 1954. Poison ivy "urushiol." Am. Chem. Soc. J. 76:2959–2965.

Taylor, P. 1962. Dozens of death-bean necklaces in city. The Ottawa Citizen (Newspaper), Sept. 12, Ottawa, Ont. p. 3.

Thomas, D.L.; Quick, M.P.; Morgan, R.P. 1987. Suspected foxglove (*Digitalis purpurea*) poisoning in a dairy cow. Vet. Rec. 120:300–301.

Thomson, R.B.; Sifton, H.B. 1922. A guide to the poisonous plants and weed seeds of Canada and the Northern United States. Univ. Toronto Press, Toronto, Ont. 159 pp.

Thorp, F., Jr.; Deem, A.W. 1938. *Suckleya suckleyana*, a poisonous plant. J. Am. Vet. Med. Assoc. new series 47:192–197.

Thorp, F., Jr.; Deem, A.W.; Harrington, H.D.; Tobiska, J.W. 1937. *Suckleya suckleyana*, a poisonous plant. Colo. State College Tech. Bull. 22. 19 pp.

Thorp, F., Jr.; Harsfield, G.S. 1938. Onion poisoning in horses. J. Am. Vet. Med. Assoc. 94:52–53.

Torell, L.A.; Cordon, H.W.; McDaniel, K.C.; McGinty, A. 1988. Economic impacts of perennial snakeweed infestations. Pages 57–69 *in* James, L.F., et al., eds. The ecology and economic impact of poisonous plants on livestock production. Westview Press, Boulder, Colo.

Trelease, S.F.; Martin, A.L. 1936. Plants made poisonous by selenium absorbed from the soil. Bot. Rev. 2:373–396.

Tucker, J.M.; Fowler, M.E.; Harvey, W.A.; Berry, L.J. 1964. Poison hemlocks. Their identification and control. Univ. Calif. Agric. Exp. Stn. Circ. 530. 19 pp.

Turner, N.J. 1978. Food plants of British Columbia Indians. Part II—Interior peoples. B.C. Prov. Mus., Victoria, Handb. 36:1–259.

Underhill, J.E. 1959. A case of hellebore poisoning. Can. Field-Nat. 73:128–129.

Van Kampen, K.R.; James, L.F. 1969. Pathology of locoweed poisoning in sheep. Pathol. Vet. 6:413–423.

Van Wijk, H.L.G. 1911. A dictionary of plant names. Martinus Nijhoff, The Hague, Netherlands. 1444 pp.

Wagnon, K.A. 1959. A study of bracken poisoning of cattle on a California forest range. J. Range Manage. 12:249–255.

Waldron, C.A. 1908. Poisoning from locust bark. Am. Vet. Rev. 33:456–459.

Waller, E.F.; Prince, F.S.; Hodgdon, A.R.; Colovos, N.S. 1944. Sensitive fern poisoning of three horses. N.H. Agric. Exp. Stn. Tech. Bull. 83. 8 pp.

Walter, W.; Khanna, P. 1972. Chemistry of the aroids I. *Dieffenbachia seguine, amoena* and *picta*. Econ. Bot. 26:364–372.

Warren, L.E. 1912. A note on the poisonous properties of *Parthenocissus quinquefolia*. Merck's Rep. 21:123.

Waud, R.A. 1940. The action of *Kalmia angustifolia* (lambkill). J. Pharmacol. Exp. Ther. 69:103–111.

Weaver, S.E.; McWilliams, E.L. 1980. The biology of Canadian weeds. 44. *Amaranthus retroflexus* L., *A. powellii* S. Wats. and *A. hybridus* L. Can. J. Plant Sci. 60:1215–1234.

Webb, L. 1948. Guide to medicinal and poisonous plants of Queensland. C.S.I.R., Melbourne, Bull. 232. 202 pp.

Weswig, P.H.; Freed, A.M.; Haag, J.R. 1946. Antithiamine activity of plant materials. J. Biol. Chem. 165:737–738.

Whitehead, E.I.; Moxon, A.L. 1952. Nitrate poisoning. South Dakota State Coll. Agric. Exp. Stn. Bull. 424. 23 pp.

Wilcox, E.V. 1897. Larkspur poisoning in sheep. Mont. Agric. Exp. Stn. Bull. 15. 51 pp.

Williams, M.C. 1983. Poisonous plants, part 3, poisonous alkaloids in plants. Weeds Today 14:6–7.

Williams, M.C.; James, L.F. 1978. Livestock poisoning from nitro-bearing *Astragalus*. Pages 379–389 *in* Keeler, R.F., et al., eds. Effects of poisonous plants on livestock. Academic Press, New York, N.Y.

Williams, M.C.; James, L.F.; Bleak, A.T. 1975. Toxicity of introduced nitro-containing *Astragalus* to sheep, cattle and chicks. J. Range Manage. 29:30–33.

Willis, C.L. 1969. Toxic constituents of the stinging nettle. M.S. Dissertation, Iowa State Univ., Ames. 42 pp. (Mimeogr.).

Wilson, T. 1924. Poisoning caused by eating daffodil bulbs. Mo. Bot. Gard. Bull. 12:52.

Wilson, V.A. 1934. Toxic properties of greasewood, with a brief discussion of the physiological action of oxalic acid and its soluble salts. J. Am. Vet. Med. Assoc. 38:76–81.

Wolf, F.A.; Curtis, R.S.; Kaupp, B.F. 1918. A monograph on trembles or milksickness and white snakeroot. N.C. Agric. Exp. Stn. Tech. Bull. 15. 74 pp.

Woolsey, J.H.; Jasper, D.E., Jr.; Cordy, D.R.; Christensen, J.F. 1952. Two outbreaks of hepatic cirrhosis in swine in California, with evidence incriminating the tarweed, *Amsinckia intermedia*. Vet. Med. 47:55–58.

Worobec, S.M.; Hickey, T.A.; Kinghorn, A.D.; Soejarto, D.D.; West, D. 1981. Irritant contact dermatitis from an ornamental (*Euphorbia hermentiana*). Contact Dermatitis 7:19–22.

Yates, G. 1915. Poisoning by woody nightshade. Vet. Rec. 28:269–270.

INDEX TO COMMON NAMES

Giant dumbcane (*Dieffenbachia amoena*), 14–15
Giant hogweed (*Heracleum mantegazzianum*), 48
Ginger, wild (*Asarum canadense*), 16
Ginkgo (*Ginkgo biloba*), 29
Glorieuse du Malabar (*Gloriosa superba*), 35–36
Glory lily (*Gloriosa superba*), 35–36
Glycérie géante (*Glyceria grandis*), 29
Glycines (*Wisteria* spp.), 34
Golden-bean (*Thermopsis rhombifolia*), 34
Golden-chain (*Laburnum anagyroides*), 32
Golden-trumpet (*Allamanda cathartica*), 12–13
Goldenrod, velvety (*Solidago mollis*), 24
Graines à chapelet (*Caulophyllum thalictroides*), 17
Grande chélidoine (*Chelidonium majus*), 38
Grande fougère (*Pteridium aquilinum*), 40
Grande oseille (*Rumex acetosa*), 40
Grass pea (*Lathyrus sativus*), 32–33
Greasewood (*Sarcobatus vermiculatus*), 20–21
Greater celandine (*Chelidonium majus*), 38
Green tansy mustard (*Descurainia pinnata*), 24–25
Ground-cherry (*Physalis peruviana*), 45
Ground-ivy (*Glechoma hederacea*), 31
Groundsel, common (*Senecio vulgaris*), 24
Guelder-rose (*Viburnum opulus*), 19
Gui de chêne (*Phoradendron flavescens*), 37
Gutierrezie faux-sarothra (*Gutierrezia sarothrae*), 22

Hairy vetch (*Vicia villosa*), 34
Hélénies (*Helenium* spp.), 22
Héliotrope obové de Curaçao (*Heliotropium curassavicum*), 18
Hellebore, false (*Veratrum viride*), 36
Hemlock, poison (*Conium maculatum*), 48
Hemp dogbane (*Apocynum cannabinum*), 13
Henbane, black (*Hyoscyamus niger*), 44–45
Herbe à la puce (*Rhus radicans*), 11–12
Herbe à poux, fausse (*Iva xanthifolia*), 23
Hogweed, giant (*Heracleum mantegazzianum*), 48
Holly, American (*Ilex opaca*), 13
Honeysuckles (*Lonicera* spp.), 18
Horse-chestnut (*Aesculus hippocastanum*), 30
Horsetails (*Equisetum* spp.), 25
Hortensia (*Hydrangea macrophylla*), 43
Hound's-tongue (*Cynoglossum officinale*), 17
Houx d'Amérique (*Ilex opaca*), 13
Hydrangea (*Hydrangea macrophylla*), 43
Hyménoxis de Richardson (*Hymenoxis richardsonii*), 22

Iceland poppy (*Papaver nudicaulis*), 38–39
Ifs (*Taxus* spp.), 46

Tulips/tulipes (*Tulipa* spp.), 36
Two-grooved milk-vetch (*Astragalus bisulcatus*), 31

Varaire vert (*Veratrum viride*), 36
Veined dock (*Rumex venosus*), 40
Verge d'or veloutée (*Solidago mollis*), 24
Vesce velue (*Vicia villosa*), 34
Vetch, hairy (*Vicia villosa*), 34
Vigne vierge (*Parthenocissus quinquefolia*), 49
Vipérine (*Echium vulgare*), 17–18
Virginia creeper (*Parthenocissus quinquefolia*), 49

Water-hemlocks (*Cicuta* spp.), 47–48
Western bleedingheart (*Dicentra formosa*), 29
Western minniebush (*Menziesia ferruginea*), 26
Western poison-oak (*Rhus diversiloba*), 11–12
Western water-hemlock (*Cicuta douglasii*), 47–48
White camas (*Zigadenus elegans*), 36–37
White rose-bay (*Rhododendron albiflorum*), 26
White snakeroot (*Eupatorium rugosum*), 21–22
Wild calla (*Calla palustris*), 14
Wild false indigo (*Baptisia leucantha*), 32
Wild ginger (*Asarum canadense*), 16
Wild indigo (*Baptisia tinctoria*), 32
Wild mustard (*Sinapis arvensis*), 25
Wild onion (*Allium canadense*), 34–35
Wild parsnip (*Pastinaca sativa*), 48
Wisterias (*Wisteria* spp.), 34

Yellow lady's-slipper (*Cypripedium calceolus*), 38
Yellow rocket (*Barbarea vulgaris*), 24
Yellow star-thistle (*Centaurea solstitialis*), 21
Yews (*Taxus* spp.), 46

Zigadènes (*Zigadenus* spp.), 36–37

INDEX TO BOTANICAL NAMES

Menziesia ferruginea, 26
Monstera deliciosa, 15

Narcissus spp., 11
Nerium oleander, 13
Nicotiana tabacum, 45

Onoclea sensibilis, 40
Ornithogalum umbellatum, 36
Oxytropis spp., 33–34

Papaver spp., 38–39
Parthenocissus quinquefolia, 49
Pastinaca sativa, 48
Phacelia campanularia, 30
Philodendron spp., 15
Phoradendron flavescens, 37
Physalis peruviana, 45
Phytolacca americana, 39
Pinus ponderosa, 39
Podophyllum peltatum, 17
Primula obconica, 41
Prunus spp., 42–43
Pteridium aquilinum, 40

Quercus spp., 28

Ranunculus bulbosus, 42
Rhamnus spp., 42
Rheum rhaponticum, 39–40
Rhododendron spp., 26
Rhus spp., 11–12
Ricinus communis, 28
Robinia pseudoacacia, 34
Rudbeckia spp., 23
Rumex spp., 40

Sambucus spp., 18–19
Sarcobatus vermiculatus, 20–21
Senecio spp., 23–24
Sinapis arvensis, 25
Solanum spp., 45
Solidago mollis, 24
Suckleya suckleyana, 21
Symphoricarpos albus, 19
Symplocarpus foetidus, 15

Taxus spp., 46
Thermopsis rhombifolia, 34